Indian

Myths  Legends

For Jeff

Published in Great Britain by Brockhampton Press,
This edition printed in 2004,
20 Bloomsbury Street, London WC1B 3JH

ISBN 1 84186 105 7

A copy of the CIP data is available from the British Library upon request.

Created and produced by Flame Tree Publishing, a part of The Foundry Creative Media Company Limited,
The Long House, Antrobus Road, Chiswick, London W4 5HY.

Cover design by Open Door Ltd, Rutland, UK.

Indian
Myths & Legends

K. E. SULLIVAN

BROCKHAMPTON PRESS

CONTENTS

INTRODUCTION

HE MYTHOLOGY OF INDIA is as vast and varied as her myriad cultures, languages and beliefs, as diverse as her philosophy and religion. Indeed, more than almost any other nation, India has intertwined her religion, literature and philosophy in a comprehensive mythology that encompasses most of her history in its breadth and vision. In India there are many languages spoken, and many religions observed. The largest of these religions is Hindu, and it is the Hindu myths that comprise the greatest proportion of the stories that appear in this book.

The study of myths has grown to gigantic proportions over the last century, and it has become clear in every aspect of cultural study that myth is intrinsic to an understanding of people, for it represents their beliefs, explains their behaviour, and provides a portrait of their customs and morality. A myth can no longer be dismissed as an entertaining bit of nonsense – time has proved that it is the crucial elements of a people's ideology which are fixed in their mythology, and its study is therefore essential to learning. For many cultures, myths touch on religion; in Indian mythology, gods play by far the most important role, presenting an explanation for religious beliefs which can be at the same time profound and difficult to comprehend.

In *Hinduism*, W. O'Flaherty wrote: 'If myths are stories about the gods, it is difficult to find a Hindu story that is not mythical. "Here there are more gods than men," a puzzled European remarked on India centuries ago, and the line between gods and men in Hinduism is as vague and ephemeral as the cloudy trail of a sky-writer. ... Gods in India are no better than men, merely more powerful. Indeed, their extraordinary powers allow them to indulge in vices on an extraordinary scale: divine power corrupts divinely.'

Indian gods are given their identities by their heritage, and their history. They form an extensive pantheon which has included and occasionally dropped names across the centuries, as the religious beliefs are expounded and transformed.

This pantheon has been recorded in many forms and in many languages, but most importantly in the great Sanskrit epic of *Mahabharata*, a poem which is the longest in any language, at 200,000 lines, and written between 400 BC and AD 200. It consists of a huge mass of legendary material which has developed around one key heroic narrative – the struggle for power between two related families, the Pandavas and the Kauravas (Kurus). At the centre of this work is the *Bhagavadgita*, which has become the national gospel of India, and the most significant religious text of Hinduism. The *Bhagavadgita* was written in the first or second century AD and comprises eighteen chapters. It takes the form of a conversation between the prince Arjuna and Krishna, who is a later incarnation of the god Vishnu. There is a philosophical discussion of the nature of God, and a compelling explanation of how he can be seen, and known.

Opposite: Indian gods are given their identities by their heritage, and their history; they form an extensive pantheon which has been altered as religious beliefs changed.

The *Mahabharata* is a fascinating and extraordinarily vivid work, singing with a characterization that is so rare in old testaments. There is an exquisite blend of characters which create a drama that has enveloped thousands of tales, each of which relates a unique perception, lesson or belief. Most importantly, however, the *Mahabharata* is entertaining, serving to teach and to work the imagination in order to put forth the fundamental beliefs of the Hindu religion.

Other great works include the *Ramayana*, written about 300 BC. This details the story of Rama and Sita – the perfect king and his wife, directly descended from the gods and the earth. This is a romantic work and less important in the development of the Indian mythology than its counterpart the *Mahabharata*, but it has nonetheless become one of the most popular scriptures of Hinduism, and acts as a gospel of purity and despair.

The *Harivamsa* (AD 400) was another important work in the combined religious and mythological structure of the Indian literature, and it was swiftly followed by the *Puranas* (AD 400 to 1000).

The *Harivamsa* works as an afterword to the *Mahabharata*, explaining the ancestry and the exploits of Krishna, together with other Hindu legends. The *Puranas*, of which eighteen survive, are extensive works examining the mythology of Hinduism, the sagas of heroes, and the legends of saints. The most significant of them, the *Bhagavata-Purana*, celebrates the god Vishnu in his many incarnations, particularly as Krishna. The *Bhagavata-Purana* has had a profound influence on almost every aspect of Indian culture – her religion, art, music and literature, and many scholars consider it the greatest poem ever written.

The Sanskrit interpretation and record of Hindu and subsequent mythology is one of the most imaginative and luxuriant of any culture; indeed, there was a belief for many years that the folktale tradition originated in India. One of the greatest collections is the *Pancatantra*, a collection of animal fables which are some of the most famous in Europe.

The central part of classical Sanskrit literature is, however, the *Vedas*, which are sacred Hindu writings from about 1400 to 1200 BC. There are also commentaries on the *Vedas* in the *Brahmanas*, the *Aranyakas*, and the *Upanishads* (1000 to 500 BC), and the epic and wisdom literature (400 BC to AD 1000).

The oldest document is the *Rig-Veda*, which is a collection of more than a thousand hymns, composed about 1400 BC. This is the most important part of early Hinduism and later became known as the *Brahmanas*. These texts did not originally take a written form; they were carried across centuries of oral communication and have been preserved with all the embellishments presented by the many translations. Hindu literature both fed and fed from the *Rig-Veda*, and much of early mythology has become synonymous with it.

Most of the myths contained within the *Rig-Veda* deal with creation – heaven and earth and what intervenes. The hymns were addressed to the Vedic gods, who included:

Agni, fire
Indra, thunder
Surya, sun
Vayu, wind
Aditi, firmament
Varuna, rain and sea
Ushas, dawn
Prithivi, earth
the Ashvins (Castor and Pullux)
Dyaus-piter, the father of light
Yama, death
Vritra, drought
Rudra, storm
Maruts, whirlwinds

The gods of the Vedic pantheon remained a part of Hindu mythology for centuries to come, although their importance was diminished by the entrance of a new and more complicated order of gods. O'Flaherty writes:

> They become literary and metaphorical fixtures rather than numinous deities. Indra is mocked for its Gargantuan sexual and alcoholic appetites, depicted as womanizer, a coward and a liar. Yama remains king of the dead, though he now functions, like Indra, as a mere pawn of the true gods, Shiva and Vishnu. The myths about these two great gods and other minor divinities of the post-Vedic period are found in Sanskrit texts composed from about 500 BC until well into the medieval period ... and frequently retold ... to the present day.

In addition to the two major divinities, Shiva and Vishnu, there are others who are still worshipped today. Many scholars argue that Vishnu and Shiva are essentially identical, and are indistinguishable from Prhama, or the creator. Shiva, a Sanskrit word meaning 'auspicious one', is a more remote god than Vishnu. Shiva is regarded as both destroyer and restorer, and he is more difficult to understand than Vishnu. Views about Shiva may have become convoluted, merging roles that were once assigned to various earlier gods. But the differences between Vishnu and Shiva lie in their presentation, for as Jan Knappert points out, 'The difference between the gods is not in their function, but in their character, their qualities. Each god, by his special nature, teaches us something about the universe that we had not seen before, because each god highlights a unique aspect of creation and with that, of our own world of dreams, our own deepest souls.'

Many animals and plants are also regarded as holy. Most notable is the cow. All cattle are protected and monkeys, tree squirrels, and some snakes are also considered hallowed. All rivers are considered sacred, but the Ganges in the north of India is the holiest of rivers because it supposedly flows from the head of Shiva.

The Vedic writers believed in a concept of heaven and hell to which the dead pass, depending on the quality of their earthly lives – something slightly akin to current-day Western beliefs. Some time after the sixth century BC, however, the belief in reincarnation was developed. Although at first confined to small groups of holy men, it soon became widely believed across the Indian continent, and explained in the *Upanishads*, a document prepared for the sole purpose of teaching a knowledge which would encourage the student to absorb a mystical knowledge that allows him to escape the rebirth cycle. The *Upanishads* are the last stage of interpretation of the *Vedas*, expounding the concept of a single supreme being, Brahman, and investigating the nature of all reality.

By the time the Buddha appeared the belief in reincarnation had been accepted and propounded into a cultural doctrine. From that time Hinduism's main concern became release from the cycle of birth and death instead of making offerings to please or pacify the gods. Sacrifice became infrequent because of an unwillingness to destroy living things. Then the primary older gods of the Vedas were slowly displaced by newer deities discussed above and to this day they are still the focus of much devotional prayer and dogma in India.

O'Flaherty points out that the Hindu teaching on divine incarnation (gods becoming flesh) made it possible for the older gods to be accepted as incarnate in the newer ones. The religious development of this period is reflected in both the *Mahabharata* and the *Ramayana*. This form of Hinduism took on the title asceticism, which was largely unknown to the religion of the *Vedas*. However, more and more young men became ascetic and gave up the trappings of modern life to become hermits and as a result asceticism took on a key part of the Hindu faith.

In the period immediately preceding the sixth century BC, Buddhism and Jainism emerged: religions centred on the monastic life. A strong emphasis on the holy life in these religions had a profound influence on Hinduism.

Buddhist teachings spread throughout their mythology, mainly through the *Pali canon*, which are the texts of early Buddhism, but also the *Jakatas*, which comprise more than 500 episodes which are said to have occurred during incarnations of Buddha, and in this fascinating collection are fairy tales, animal stories and ballads.

Among the heresies of the Kali Age, which was said to have begun when Krishna died, O'Flaherty says that:

> Buddhism was regarded by Hindus of the ancient period as the prime thread, and it was as the Buddha that Vishnu became incarnate after the death of Krishna. Later Hindus have seen in this avatar an attempt at rapprochement with Buddhism, but the avatar was originally designed to damn the Buddhists in Hindu eyes; for Vishnu was said to assume the form of Buddha to mislead, corrupt and ultimately destroy dangerous demons, who were indestructible as long as they remained steadfast in the practice of orthodox Buddhism.

A basic understanding of these two religions helps to unravel the complicated philosophy behind the myths and legends outlined in this book. Although Buddhism does make up only about four per cent of all Indians, its place in history and in literature is undoubted, and its traditions continue to flourish today.

Hinduism, which makes up more than eighty per cent of current Indian religious practice is believed to have spawned in a developed civilization in the Indus Valley, about 2300 BC. This civilization had its own religion, which was transformed when they were invaded about 1500 BC. The invading civilization was the Aryans, and the combined religious dogma was the basis for what we now consider to be ancient Hinduism.

W. J. Wilkins, in *Hindu Mythology* points out that it was a religion of the household, of veneration for ancestors, and of devotion to the world spirit (Brahman):

> The Aryans had numerous gods, nearly all of whom were male. But the Aryans made no images or pictures of their gods as later Hinduism has done. Aryan worship was centred around the sacrificial fire at home, while later Hinduism worshipped in temples. The complex ceremony of the Aryans involved sacrifice of animals. Hymns were composed for these rituals, and it is in the collections of the hymns, which are, of course, the *Vedas*, and it was under their influence that the earliest Hinduism developed.

For the first 200 years after the Buddha's death, Buddhism was a local religion. When King Asoka converted to Buddhism in the third century BC, he used his resources to spread the religion. Trade between India, China, and the Roman Empire brought Indian people and their religions to China. By the fifth century AD, there was very little evidence of the religion in India itself, as it was carried further east. By 1200 a Muslim dynasty had come to power in India, and Buddhism virtually disappeared from the land of its origin. Hinduism does, however, still contain many ideas borrowed from Buddhism, which have enhanced and made it one of the richest religions in the world. Their mythology, certainly in the earliest years, has become largely interchangeable.

Although many gods may be worshipped, modern Hindus are generally divided into followers of Vishnu, Shiva, or Shakti. Nearly all Hindus look upon one of these as an expression of the ultimate being, the one in charge of the destiny of the universe.

Opposite:
An understanding of these two religions helps to unravel the complicated philosophy behind the myths and legends.

Each of the followers holds the *Vedas* in high regard, and has its own scriptures. In the *Bhagavadgita*, for example, Vishnu is honoured in his incarnation Krishna. Another incarnation, Rama, is the hero of the *Ramayana*. Vishnu is the protector and preserver of the world, and he is worshipped by many cults in various forms besides Krishna and Rama.

It is the rich and varied tradition of folktales and fables which have illuminated the mythological fabric of the Indian culture; indeed, every great epic is in fact a compilation of didactic stories, legends, fairy tales and ancient narratives from across the continent. Alongside is an extensive and pervading respect for and acceptance of religion and spirituality. Somewhere, down the annals of history, the two have become intertwined, giving Indian mythology a pedigree unlike any other, and Indian religion a series of parables that bring it alive – probably partly explaining its extraordinary popularity today. And now, even the most emancipated of Hindus believe their mythology is a valid and genuine series of events – because, in many ways, it is.

Opposite:
The great epics are in fact compilations of didactic stories, legends, fairy tales and ancient narratives; they speak of battles which may actually have occurred.

AUTHOR'S NOTE

The myths, legends, folktales and stories in this book are mainly drawn from the *Ramayana*, and to a lesser extent the *Mahabharata*, and stories from the *Puranas*, the *Vedas* and other Indian epics. Many of the more notable tales have been omitted in favour of presenting a fuller taste of the magnificent epic, the *Ramayana*. Other works are represented here to give a wider perspective of the mythological fabric of India, but their brevity do not do justice to the full works. I am grateful for the invaluable interpretations of Ananda K. Coomaraswamy and Sister Nivedita (1913), who have been quoted extensively in the stories which follow; theirs are some of the most sensitive and learned translations of some of India's finest epics and tales. Other sources of note include W. J. Wilkins' *Hindu Mythology* and *An Illustrated Encyclopedia of Mythology* (ed. Richard Cavendish).

TALES OF
THE RAMAYANA

he *Ramayana* was an epic poem of about 50,000 lines, which was originally composed by the hermit Valmiki, probably in the third century. Many versions of this great work exist across India where Rama, the seventh incarnation of Vishnu, and hero of the poem, was worshipped. The *Ramayana* was originally divided into seven books, each of which celebrated a part of Rama's life. Rama was the greatest human hero of Hindu mythology, the son of a king and the avatar of Vishnu. He was the model of every good man, for he was brave, chivalrous, well versed and virtuous. He had but one wife and his name has become synonymous with loyalty and fidelity in many parts of the Indian nation.

It is believed that this epic poem is cleansing – even a reading of the *Ramayana* will remove the sins of the reader, for the text itself is regarded as charismatic. Many events befell Rama in his earthly form, and he left behind two sons. The following tales represent some of the most fascinating and profound occurrences in the life of Rama, whose name, even today, is in many parts of the Hindu community, the word for 'God'.

The Birth of Rama

King Dasharatha, thus cried they,
Fervent in penance many a day,
The sacrificial steed has slain,
Longing for sons, but all in vain.
Now, at the cry of us forlorn,
Incarnate as his seed be born.
Three queens has he; each lovely dame
Like Beauty, Modesty, or Fame.
Divide thyself in four, and be
His offspring by these noble three;
Man's nature take, and slay in fight
Ravana, who laughs at heavenly might:
This common scourge, this rankling thorn,
Whom the three worlds too long have borne.

THE *RAMAYANA*, GRIFFITHS

ONCE, LONG, LONG AGO, in the great city of Ayodhya there lived a king. Ayodhya was a prosperous city, one where its citizens were happy, pure of heart and well educated in the teachings of both man and god. Its king was also a good man and happy in almost every respect, for he had many wise counsellors and sages in his family and he had been blessed with a lovely daughter, Santa. This king was called Dasharatha, and he married his sweet daughter to the great sage Rishyasringa, who became a member of his inner circle, advising him on all matters with great wisdom and foresight. Two fine priests – Vashishtha and Vamadeva – were also part of his family, and they were known to all as the most saintly of men.

But Dasharatha had one hole in his glittering life; he longed for a son to carry on his line, a son who would one day be king. For many years he made offerings to the great powers, but to no avail, until such time as he made the most supreme sacrifice, that of a horse. His three wives were overjoyed by the prospect of having a son and when, after one year, the horse returned from the sacrifice, Rishyasringa and Vashishtha prepared the ceremony. With the greatest of respect and joy Rishyasringa was able to announce to Dasharatha that he would father four sons, and they would carry his name into the future.

Opposite: Its king was also a good man and happy in almost every respect, for he had many wise counsellors in his family and had been blessed with a lovely daughter.

When any sacrifice is made by man, all of the deities come together to take their portion of what has been offered, and so it was on this occasion that they had assembled to take from the sacrificial horse. There was, however, a dissenter among their ranks, one who was greedy

and oppressive, and who caused in his colleagues such dissension that they came forward to Brahma with a request that he be destroyed. The evil rakshasa was called Ravana, and at an early age he had been granted immunity from death by yakshas, rakshasas or gods. His immunity had led him to become selfish and arrogant, and he took great pleasure in flaunting his exemption from the normal fates. Brahma spoke wisely to the gathered deities.

'Ravana is indeed evil,' he said quietly, ' and he had great foresight in requesting immunity from death by his equals. But,' and here Brahma paused. 'But,' he went on, ' he was not wise enough to seek immunity from death by humans – and it is in this way that he must be slain.'

The deities were relieved to find that Ravana was not invincible, and as they celebrated amongst themselves, they were quietened by a profound presence who entered their midst. It was the great God Vishnu himself, and he appeared in flowing yellow robes, his eyes sparkling. He carried with him mace, and discus and conch, and he appeared on the back of Garuda, the divine bird attendant of Narayana. The deities fell at his feet, and they begged him to be born as Dasharatha's four sons in order to destroy the deceitful Ravana.

And so it was that Vishnu threw himself into Dasharatha's fire and taking the form of a sacred tiger, spoke to the anxious father-to-be, pronouncing himself the ambassador of God himself. He presented Dasharatha with spiritual food, which he was to share with his wives – two portions to Sumitra, one to Kaikeyi, and one to Kaushalya. And soon, four strong, healthy babies were born to Dasharatha's wives and they were named by Vashishtha, the divine priest. They were Rama, born to Kaushalya, Bharata, born to Kaikeyi, and Lakshman and Satrughna born to Sumitra.

Rama and Vashishtha

DASHARATHA'S FOUR SONS GREW into robust and healthy young men. They were brave and above all good, and they were revered for their looks and good sense. The greatness of Vishnu was spread amongst them, and each glowed with great worth. The young men travelled in pairs – Satrughna devoting himself to his brother Bharata, and Lakshman dedicating himself to Rama. Rama was very much the favoured son, favourite of both Dasharatha and the people. He was a noble

youth, well-versed in arts, sciences and physical applications alike; his spirituality was evident in all he did. By the age of sixteen, Rama was more accomplished than any man on earth, inspiring greatness in all who came into contact with him.

There lived, at this time, a rishi by the name of Vishvamitra who had become a brahma-rishi, an excellent status which had been accorded to him by the gods themselves. He lived in Siddhashrama, but his life there was far from easy. He was a religious man, and took enormous strength from his daily prayers and sacrifices. Each day his sacrificial fires and prayers were interrupted by two wily and evil rakshasas, Maricha and Suvahu, who received their orders from Ravana himself. Knowing that Rama was the incarnation of Vishnu, Vishvamitra approached Dasharatha and begged him to send Rama to rid him of these evil spirits.

Now Dasharatha was against the idea of sending his favourite son on what would surely be a dangerous and perhaps fatal mission, but he knew as well that a great brahma-rishi must be respected. And so it was that Rama and Lakshman travelled to Vishvamitra for ten days, in order to stand by the sacrificial fire. The young men were dressed in the finest of clothes, glittering with jewels and fine cloths. They were adorned with carefully wrought arms, and they glowed with pride and valour. All who witnessed their passing was touched by the glory, and a ray of light entered each of their lives

They arrived at Siddhashrama in a cloud of radiance, and as the sacrifice began, Rama wounded Maricha and Suvahu, until they fled in dismay. The other evil spirits were banished, and the little hermitage was once again in peace, cleansed of the evil of Ravana.

Rama and the Bow of Janaka

RAMA WAS GREETED WITH GREAT ACCLAIM after he rid Vishvamitra's hermitage of the evil spirits, and his taste of heroism whetted in him a great appetite for further adventure. He begged Vishvamitra to present him with further tasks, and he was rewarded by the hallowed priest's plans to visit Janaka, the Raja of Mithila.

Janaka was owner of a splendid bow, one which no man was able to string. He had come by this bow through his ancestor, Devarata, who had received it personally from the gods, who had themselves been presented the bow by Shiva. The bow was now worshipped by all who

Opposite:
They arrived at Siddhashrama in a cloud of radiance, just as the sacrifice was to begin.

had seen it, for gods, rakshasas and even the finest warriors had been unable to bend its mighty back.

Janaka was planning a marvellous sacrifice, and it was for Mithila that the three men would depart, in order to take part in the festivities, and to see the great bow in person. As they travelled along the Ganges, they were followed by all the birds and animals who inhabited Siddhashrama, and by the monkey protectors who had been presented to the two brothers upon their birth. They arrived in Mithila in a burst of splendid colour and radiance, and Janaka knew at once that the company he was about to keep was godly in every way. He bowed deeply to the men, and set them carefully among the other men of nobility.

The following day, Janaka brought the men to the bow, and explained to them its great significance.

He said to Rama, 'I have a daughter, Sita, who is not the product of man, or of animal, but who burst from a furrow of the earth itself as I ploughed and hallowed my field. She is a woman of supreme beauty and godliness, and she will be presented to any man or god who can bend the bow.'

Rama and his brother bent their heads respectfully, and Rama nodded towards the bow. A chariot pulled by four thousand men moved the bow forward, and he quietly reached towards it. The case sprung open at his touch, and as he strung it, it snapped into two pieces with a bolt of fire. There was a crack so loud that all the men in the room, bar Rama, Vishvamitra, Janaka and Lakshman, fell to the ground, clutching their ears and writhing. And there was silence – a quiet brought on by fear and reverence. The spectators struggled to their knees and bowed to the great Rama, and a jubilant Janaka shouted his blessing and ordered the wedding preparations to begin. Messengers were sent at once to the household of Dasharatha, and upon his arrival, the festivities began.

Sita was presented to Rama, and Urmila, the second daughter of Janaka was promised to Lakshman. Mandavya and Srutakirti, who were daughters of Kushadhwaja, were presented to Bharata and Satrughna. All around, the world erupted in a fusion of light and colour – fragrant blossoms were cast down from the heavens upon the radiant brothers and their brides, and a symphony of angelic music wove its way around them. There was happiness like none ever known, and the four young men cast down their heads with deep gratitude. They returned home, in a shower of glory, to Ayodhya, where they would serve their proud and honoured father, Dasharatha.

Opposite:
The men departed for Mithila, in order to take part in the festivities, and to see the great bow in person.

Kaikeyi and the Heir Apparent

AFTER MANY YEARS OF HAPPINESS at Ayodhya, Dasharatha decided that the time had come to appoint an heir apparent. Rama was still the most favoured of the brothers, a fine man of sterling integrity and wisdom. He was known across the land for his unbending sense of justice, and he was friend to any man who was good. His brothers had no envy for their honourable brother for he was so kind and serene that he invited their good intentions and they wished him nothing but good fortune. Rama was the obvious choice for heir, and Dasharatha took steps to prepare for his ascendance.

He drew together all of his counsellors and kings, and he advised them of his plans. He explained how his years had been kind and bounteous, but that they weighed down on him now, and he felt the need to rest. He proposed that his son Rama become heir apparent. The uproar astonished the elderly king. There was happiness and celebration at his proposal, and at once the air grew clear and the skies shone with celestial light. Bemused, he turned to the esteemed parliament of men and he said, 'Why, why do you wish him to be your ruler?'

'By reason of his many virtues, for indeed he towers among men as Sakra among the gods. He speaks the truth and he is a mighty and even bowman. He is ever busied with the welfare of the people, and not given to detraction where he finds one blemish among many virtues. He is skilled in music and his eyes are fair to look upon. Neither his pleasure nor his anger is in vain; he is easily approached, and self-controlled, and goes not forth to war or the protection of a city or province without victorious return. He is beloved of all. Indeed, the Earth desires him for her lord.' And once again the cheers rose and the preparations began.

The finest victuals were ordered – honey and butter, rices and milk and curds. There were golds, silvers and gems of great gleaming weight, and elephants and bulls and tigers ordered. Fine cloths and skins were draped around the palace, and everyone hummed with incessant, bustling excitement. And above it all was Rama, serene and calm, as cool as the winter waters of the Ganges, as pure of heart as the autumn moon. And just before the time when he would stand forward in his father's shoes, he was brought before the great Dasharatha, who greeted his kneeling form with warmth and lifted him up upon the seat of kings. He said to him then:

Opposite:
The finest victuals were ordered – honey and butter, rices and milk and curds. Everyone hummed with incessant, bustling excitement.

'Though thou art virtuous by nature, I would advise thee out of love and for thy good: Practise yet greater gentleness and restraint of sense; avoid all lust and anger; maintain thy arsenal and treasury; personally and by means of others make thyself well acquainted with the affairs of state; administer justice freely to all, that the people may rejoice. Gird thee, my son, and undertake thy task.'

Rama, for all his wisdom, found great solace in his father's words, and as the town around him buzzed with the activity of thousands of men preparing for the holy fast, he sat calmly, in worship and in gratitude.

Now throughout this time, all of Dasharatha's household celebrated the choice of Rama for heir apparent – his mother, Kaushalya, and his wife, Sita, were honoured, and his aunts, too, revelled in their relation to this fine young man. There was no room for envy in their hearts, until, that is, the deceitful old nurse, Manthara, took it upon herself to stir up the seeds of discontent. And this she did by the subtle but constant pressures she applied to her mistress, Kaikeyi, the mother of Bharata.

Kaikeyi was by nature a fair woman, easy natured and gentle. It took many months of persuasion before a hole was pierced in her goodness, and the beginnings of evil allowed to enter. It was a misfortune for Rama to become king, said Manthara, for Bharata would be cast out and Kaikeyi would be the subordinate of Kaushalya. Kaikeyi dismissed such nonsense and carried on with her daily work. Several days later, Manthara was back. Bharata would be sent away, she said. Did that not worry his mother? But Kaikeyi was calm. She said, 'Why grieve at Rama's fortune?' she said. 'He is well fitted to be king; and if the kingdom be his, it will also be Bharata's for Rama ever regards his brothers as himself.'

Manthara did not give up. She twisted her sword a little deeper and was rewarded by hitting at Kaikeyi's pride. 'Don't you know, Kaikeyi,' she said, 'that Rama's mother will seek to revenge on thee that slight that thou didst once put on her. Yours will be a sorry lot when Rama rules the earth.'

Kaikeyi's rage burst from within her and she stalked around her chambers.

'Why, he will have to be deported at once,' she said furiously. 'But how can I do it? How can I install Bharata as heir?'

The treacherous Manthara was again at her side, needling the pain and fury that she had inspired in her gentle mistress.

'You have two unused gifts from Dasharatha,' she reminded her. 'Have you forgotten that fateful day when you found him near dead on

Opposite:
Kaikeyi was by nature a fair woman, and it took many months of pressure before the old nurse Manthara was able to pierce her goodness.

the battlefield? What did he promise you then, my mistress?' she asked her. 'Why, he has made you his favourite of wives and he has done everything in his power to keep you happy. This is what you must do.' And the evil witch leaned forward and whispered in Kaikeyi's ear. Her eyes widened, and their glitter dimmed. She bowed her head and she left the room.

Kaikeyi cast off her jewels and fine clothes, and pulled down her hair. She dressed herself in sacks and she laid down on the floor of the anger chamber where she cried with such vigour that Dasharatha could not fail to hear her sobs. Finding her there, stripped of her finery, he lay beside her and spoke gently to his favourite wife.

'What has happened. What is it?' he whispered. 'If you are ill, there are many doctors who can cure what ails you. If someone has wronged you, we can right that wrong. Indeed, whatever you want, my dear Kaikeyi, I will ensure you have. Your desire is mine. You know that I can refuse you nothing.'

Kaikeyi sat up and brushed away her tears. 'You know,' she said, 'that you promised me that day long ago, when I carried you from the battlefield and administered your wounds, when I saved you from the jaws of death, you know, dear husband, that you promised me two gifts, two boons. You told me then that I could have my desire and until this day I have asked you for nothing.'

Dasharatha roared with approval. 'Of course, dear wife,' he said. 'Whatever you wish, it shall be yours. This I swear on Rama himself.'

'I wish,' she said softly, 'I wish, as Heaven and Earth and Day and Night are my witness, I wish that Bharata become heir and that Rama is cast out, clad only in deer-skins, to lead the life of a hermit in the forests of Dandaka, and that he remain there for fourteen years.'

Kaikeyi knew that in fourteen years her own son, who was good and true, could bind himself to the affections of the people and that Rama, upon his return, could not shift him from a well-regarded throne. Her plan was about to unfold and she shivered with anticipation. As expected, her husband let out a mighty roar and sank down to his knees once again. He begged Kaikeyi to change her mind, and he pleaded with her to allow his son to stay with him, but she refused to relent.

And so it was that Rama was summoned to the weeping Dasharatha, and as he travelled, the crowds rose to greet him, feeling their lives changed in some small way by the benefit of his smile, his wave, his celestial presence. And bolstered by the adoration, and glowing with the supreme eloquence of his righteousness, he entered his father's chamber with unwitting happiness and calm. His father's distress wiped the smile from his lips, and the clouds filled the autumn sky.

'What is it father,' he asked, sensing deep grief and misfortune. But his father could only mutter, 'Rama, Rama, I have wronged thee.'

Rama turned to Kaikeyi, 'Mother, mother,' he asked, 'what ill has overcome my father?'

And Kaikeyi uttered with pride and something approaching glee, 'Nothing, Rama, but your imminent downfall. He cannot frame the words that will cause you distress and unhappiness, but you must do as he asks. You must help him to fulfil his promise to me. You see, Rama, long ago he promised me two gifts. If you swear to me now that you will do as he wishes, I will tell you all.'

Rama spluttered with indignation. 'Of course, dear Mother. Anything for my father. I would walk in fire. I would drink poison, or blood, for him. Tell me now, so that I may more quickly set about easing his poor soul.'

Kaikeyi related to him the story of her gifts from Dasharatha, and told him of his father's decision that he should be sent away to dwell as a hermit in Dandaka forest for fourteen years. Bharata, she said, would be installed as heir at once.

Rama smiled warmly and with such sincerity that Kaikeyi was stung with shame. 'Of course,' he said serenely, 'I am only sad for my father, who is suffering so. Send at once for Bharata while I go to the forest. Allow me some time to comfort my mother, and Sita, and I shall do as you wish.'

He saluted Kaikeyi, and he left at once. His mother was grieved by her son's fate, but she lifted her head high and she swore to him that she would follow him. 'My darling,' she said, 'I shall follow you to the forest even as a cow follows her young. I cannot bear to wait here for your return and I will come with thee.'

Lakshman was greatly angered by the decision, and he vowed to fight for his brother who had been so wronged. But Rama calmed them both, and he spoke wisely and confidently.

'Gentle brother, I must obey the order of my father. I will never suffer degradation if I honour the words of my father.' Rama paused and turned to Kaushalya. 'Mother,' he said, taking her hands, 'Kaikeyi has ensnared the king, but if you leave him while I am gone he will surely die. You must remain and serve him. Spend your time in prayer, honouring the gods and the Brahmans and your virtue will be preserved.'

Sita greeted his news with dignity. 'I too will go forth into the forest with my husband,' she said. 'A wife shares in her husband's fate and I shall go before thee, treading upon thorns and prickly grass, and I shall be happy there as in my own father's house, thinking only of thy service.'

And Rama granted Sita her desire, and he said to her, 'Oh, my fair wife, since you do not fear the forest, you shall follow me and share my righteousness. Make haste, for we go at once.'

Rama's Exile

LAKSHMAN COULD NOT BEAR to remain in his father's home without Rama and he too decided to leave with Rama and Sita for the forest, shunning the wealth and entrapments of his lifestyle to take a part of Rama's righteousness. There was hysteria in the household as the three prepared to leave, and a noble Brahman named Sumantra threw himself on the mercy of Kaikeyi to give in, begging her to allow Rama to remain. But Kaikeyi's will had turned her heart to stone and she refused all requests for clemency. Dasharatha sat dully, numbed by grief and shame at his wife's ill will. He motioned to send all his own wealth, and that of his city, with Rama into the forest, but Kaikeyi stood firm and insisted that Dasharatha stick to his vows and send Rama into the forest as a beggar.

As their new clothes of bark were set out for them, Sita collapsed and wept – fearing for her future and loathe to give up the easiness of her life, to which she had been both born and bred. The loyal subjects of Dasharatha begged him to allow Rama's wife to take the throne in his stead – there is no one, they said, who did not love Rama, and they would honour his wife as deeply as they honoured him. Yet again, Kaikeyi resisted all suggestions.

But then Dasharatha stood tall and he spoke firmly, drawing strength from his conviction. Sita shall not go without her jewels, and her robes, he commanded. So Sita's worldly goods were returned to her, and she shone like the sun in a summer sky, flanked by the bark-clad brothers whose goodness caused them to shine with even greater glory than Sita in her finery. They climbed up onto their chariot and set off for the forest, the citizens of Ayodhya falling in front of the carriage with despair.

Opposite:
Rama would be joined by Lakshman as they set out for the forest; the brothers had shared everything since birth and could not live apart.

And then Dasharatha turned to his wife Kaikeyi, and with all of his kingly disdain he cursed her, and cast her from his bed and his home.

'Take me to Kaushalya,' he said majestically. 'Take me swiftly for it is only there that I will find peace.'

At the same time, Lakshman, Sita and Rama had made their way from the city and had reached the shores of the blessed Ganga, a river as clear as the breath of the god, and inhabited by gods and angels alike. They were greeted there by Guha, the king of Nishadha, who fed their horses and made them comfortable for the night. Rama and his brother requested a paste of grain and water and they formed their hair into the customary locks of the forest hermits. The following night they slept by a great tree on the far bank of the Ganges, and the two brothers spoke quietly to one another, pledging to protect and care for the other, and for Sita. Rama expressed his great grief at leaving his father, and his concern for Ayodhya. He begged Lakshman to return in order to care for Kaushalya, but Lakshman gently rebuked him.

'Oh Rama,' he said softly, 'I can no more live without you than a fish can taken out of water – without you I do not wish to see my father, nor Sumitra, nor Heaven itself.' The two men slept silently, comforted by their love and devotion for one another. There was only one way to get through the years ahead, and that was as a united twosome.

The following day they reached the hermitage of Bharadwaja, where the great rishi told them of a wonderful place on the mountain of Chitrakuta, a place which teemed with trees, and peacocks and elephants, where there were rivers and caves and springs and many fruits and roots on which to feed. It was a place befitting their stature, he said, and they would be safe there. And so the following morning they set off, crossing the Jamna by raft and arriving at Shyama. There they prayed and set about building a house of wood, next to the hermitage of Valmiki.

A deer was slain by Lakshman, and a ritual sacrifice was offered to the divinities. And then they settled in together and allowed the happiness of their new life to enter their souls, banishing their grief for what they had left behind.

Bharata is King

DASHARATHA WAS A BROKEN MAN, and it was not long before his grief stripped him of his life. He died in the arms of Kaushalya, bewildered by his fate and recalling an incident which had occurred once in the forest, when as a youth he had accidentally slain a hermit with an errant arrow. Dasharatha had been spared punishment by a kind rishi, but he had been warned then that he would one day meet his death grieving for his son. That memory now clung to his mind, suffocating it until he gave in to his untimely death.

Ayodhya was in mourning for the loss of their finest son Rama, and the death of their king was a blow they could scarcely fathom. There was no rain and the earth dried up; an arid curse lay over the land and the dead Dasharatha's people could not even find the energy to go about their daily toil without the wisdom and leadership of the great and wise king. An envoy was half-heartedly sent for Bharata, with a message that he must return at once, but the people cared little about his arrival, and he was not told about the fate of his father and his brother Rama.

On the seventh day, Bharata, son of Kaikeyi, arrived at Ayodhya at sunrise, the first rays of morning failing to light the dark silence that the city had become. He entered his father's palace, and finding no one awake, entered the bed chamber, which he too found empty. And then Kaikeyi appeared, glowing with vanity and pride at her new position.

'Your father is gone,' she said crisply, caring little about the man who had once been her great love. Her son had taken her place in her affections, and she lusted now for the power that he was in the position to accord her.

Bharata wept silently for his father, and then, lifting a weary head, asked quietly, 'Where is Rama, I am happy for him. Was he present to perform the death-bed rites? Where is he, mother? I am his servant. I take refuge at his feet. Please inform him that I am here. I wish to know my father's last words.'

'Blessed are they that see Rama and the strong-armed Lakshman returning here with Sita,' said Kaikeyi. 'That is what he said.'

Bharata looked at her for a moment and paused. 'Where, may I ask, are Lakshman, Rama and Sita,' he asked then, his face losing colour.

'Rama has taken Sita and Lakshman and they have been exiled to Dandaka forest,' she said nobly, and then spilling over with the excitement of her conquest, she poured out the whole story to her son, explaining the wishes granted her by Dasharatha and the wonderful honours which would now be his.

'You are a murderer,' cried Bharata and leapt to his feet, casting his mother to one side. 'I loved Rama. I loved my father. It is for their sake alone that I call you mother, that I do not renounce you now. I do not want the kingdom. I want Rama – and I intend to bring him back from the forest! At once!'

Taking only the days necessary to prepare the funeral rites and to mourn his dead father, Bharata prepared to set out to find his brother. His tears were shared for his father and for his dear brother and he resolved to find him as soon as he could. He refused the throne which was offered to him by the ministers and preparing his chariots, he rode quickly towards the forest, following in the footsteps of Rama and the others. He reached him quickly, and was shocked and dismayed to find that Rama had adorned himself in the dress of a hermit – shaggy locks framed his pale face, and he wore the skin of a black deer upon his shoulders. But that pale face was serene, and he gently wiped away his brother's tears.

'Bharata,' he said, 'I cannot return. I have been commanded by both my father and my mother to live in the forest for fourteen years. That I must do. You must rule, as our father would have wished.'

Bharata thought for a moment. 'If it was our father's will for me to have the kingdom in your place, then I have the right to bestow it upon you.'

Rama smiled kindly then, and shook his head. 'The kingdom is yours, Bharata. Rule it wisely. For these fourteen years I shall live here as a hermit.'

Bharata took his brother's sandals and it was agreed that in fourteen years he would be joined by Rama, and that the sandals would be restored to him then – with the government and kingship of Ayodhya herself.

Opposite:
Bharata arrived with many men, and demanded that Rama return to head the kingdom.

And Rama, Sita and Lakshman waved their farewells to Bharata and his men, and then they turned to leave themselves, no longer content in a house that had been trampled by feet of the outside world. They drew themselves deeper into Dandaka, where the cool darkness of the forest beckoned.

The Golden Deer

FOR TEN YEARS RAMA, SITA AND LAKSHMAN wandered through the forests of Dandaka, resting and living for spells with hermits and other men of wisdom along their path. They befriended a vulture, Jatayu, who claimed to have been a friend of Dasharatha, and he pledged to guard Sita, and to offer Rama and Lakshman his help. They settled finally at Panchavati, by the river Godaveri, where lush blossoms hung over the rippling waters and the air was filled with the verdant scent of greenery. Sita, Rama and Lakshman lived happily there, in the green, fecund woodland, and lived virtually as gods, and undisturbed, until one day they were set upon by an evil rakshasi, sister of Ravana called Surpanakha. There ensued a terrible battle when this ugly sister sought to seduce Rama and Lakshman chased her away, cutting off her ears and nose in the process.

Surpanakha fled deep into the forest, angered and bleeding and she stumbled upon her brother Khara who flew into such a rage at his sister's plight that he set out for Rama's clearing, taking fourteen thousand rakshasas with him – each of which was great, courageous and more horrible in appearance that any rakshasa before him.

Rama had been warned of their coming by Jatayu and was prepared, sending Lakshman and Sita to a secret cave and fighting the rakshasas alone, slaying each of the fourteen thousand evil spirits until at last he stood face to face with Khara. Their battle was fierce and bloody, but Rama stood his ground. At last Khara was consumed by a fiery arrow. And there was silence.

Now far from this scene Ravana was brought news of his sister's maiming and his brother's death. He was filled with such a rage that he plotted to destroy Rama by secreting away Sita. Ravana sought the advice of his most horrible accomplice, Maricha, who counselled him. Ravana was insistent that he could slay Rama single-handedly, and he ignored Maricha's advice to avoid meddling with Rama who could, if angered, quite easily destroy Ravana's city of Lanka.

Ravana's plan was put into action and the unwilling Maricha took on the form of a golden deer, with horn-like jewels and ears like two rich blue lotus flowers. He entered the forest clearing, where he flitted between the trees, golden hide glinting. As expected, Sita looked up and cried out with delight. She called to Rama and to Lakshman and she begged them to catch the deer for her pleasure. Rama, too,

Opposite:
Sita caught sight of the deer and begged Rama to catch it for her. And so he set off into the forest, leaving Lakshman to guard his wife.

suspecting nothing, was enchanted by the deer's beauty, and set out to catch her. He began to give chase.

Lakshman stayed behind, suspicious about the extraordinary beauty of the deer, where he kept watch over Sita. There was silence until, from the darkness of the woods, came the cry, 'Sita, Lakshman.'

The words were spoken in Rama's own voice, but they came from the body of the golden deer who had been hit by Rama's arrow. As the deer died he took on the shape of Maricha once again and in a last attempt to lure Lakshman from the forest clearing, he called out as Rama himself. And then he was dead.

Rama moved swiftly, realizing the ruse, but the cry had worked its magic. Lakshman was sent out into the forest by Sita, who feared for Rama's safety, and as that brave one made his way back to Panchavati, Sita was left alone.

Rama and Sita

ALONE IN CLEARING OF PANCHAVATI, Sita paced restlessly, concern for her husband and his brother growing ever greater as the moments passed. And then she was startled by a movement in the trees. Into the clearing came a wandering yogi, and Sita smiled her welcome. She would not be alone after all.

She offered the yogi food and water, and told him her identity. She kindly asked for information in return and was startled when he called himself Ravana, and asked her to renounce Rama and become his wife. Ravana gazed at the lovely Sita and a deep jealousy and anger filled his soul. He determined to have her and he cared little now for his revenge of Rama.

Now Sita was enraged by the slight afforded her husband, the great Rama, by this insolent Ravana and she lashed out at him:

'I am the servant of Rama alone, lion among men, immovable as any mountain, as vast as the great ocean, radiant as Indra. Would you draw the teeth from a lion's mouth? Or swim in the sea with a heavy stone about your neck? You are as likely to seek the sun or moon as you are me, for Rama is little like thee – he is as different as is the lion from the jackal, the elephant from the cat, the ocean from the tiny stream and gold from silver.' She stopped, fear causing her to tremble.

Ravana roared into the empty clearing, and taking his own shape

Opposite:
Ravana returned Sita to his palace and begged her to become his wife. When she refused, she was locked in a marble palace in the trees.

once again, grabbed the lovely Sita by the hair and made to rise into the air with her. His cry woke the great vulture Jatayu, who had been sleeping in a nearby tree. He rose in outrage and warned the evil spirit of the wrath of Rama, who would certainly let no spirit live who had harmed his most prized possession. But Ravana sprang upon the poor great bird and after a heroic battle, cut away his wings, so that he fell down near death.

Ravana swept Sita into his carriage and rose into the sky. As she left the clearing, Sita cried out to the flowers, and the forest, begging them to pass on her fate to Rama and Lakshman upon their return. And then she cast down her veil and her jewels as a token for her husband.

Ravana returned her to his palace and begged her to become his wife. Her face crumpled in bitter pain and she refused to speak. And as he persisted, she turned to him then and prophesied his certain death at the hands of Rama. And she spoke no more.

Rama returned from the chase of the golden deer with an overwhelming sense of trepidation, and as he met with his brother, far from the clearing, his fears were confirmed. Rama and Lakshman raced towards the hermitage, but Sita had gone. There they found the weapons which had cut down the brave Jatayu, and the dying bird, who raised himself just enough to recount the events of the previous hours. And then, released of his burden, the soul of the great Jatayu rose above the clearing, leaving his body to sag to the ground below.

And so it was that Rama set out with Lakshman to search for Sita, travelling across the country but hearing little news and having no idea where Ravana kept his palace. He met with Sugriva, a king who had been robbed of his wife and his kingdom by his cruel brother Vali, and with the help of Hanuman, chief of the monkeys they continued their search.

Sugriva and Rama formed an alliance and it was agreed that Sugriva would be restored to his throne with the help of Rama. In return Sugriva would put at his disposal the monkey host, to find the poor Sita, already four months lost.

Rama's signet ring was put in Hanuman's possession, to show to Sita as a sign when he found her, but the monkey chief returned with his host, ashamed and saddened that they had been unable to find the beautiful princess. But then, as hope began to fade, there was news. On the coasts of the sea, where the monkeys sat deep in dejection, was a cave in which an old and very wise vulture made his home. He was Sampati, and he was brother to Jatayu. When he heard of his

Opposite: Rama set out with Lakshman to search for Sita, travelling across the country but hearing little news and having no idea where Ravana kept his palace.

brother's fate he offered to the host his gift of foresight. Ravana, he announced, was with Sita in Lanka.

A brave and noble monkey, Jambavan, chose Hanuman for the task of retrieving Sita, and Hanuman swelled with pride at the prospect of his task. He sprang easily across the thousands of leagues, and across the sea — carelessly knocking down any foe who stood in his path. And so it was that he arrived on the walls of Lanka, and made his way towards the palace. The moon sat high in the sky, and the occupants of the golden city went about their nightly activities.

Making himself invisible, he entered the private apartments of Ravana, who lay sleeping with his many wives around him. But there was no sign of Sita. Hanuman roamed the city, increasingly anxious for the safety of Rama's wife, but she was not to be found. A deep desolation overtook him and he realized the enormity of his task. If he was unable to find the beautiful Sita then Lakshman and Rama would surely die of grief. And Bharata and Satrughna would die too. And the shame that would be brought on Sugriva, and the monkey host – it was too great to contemplate. Hanuman gritted his teeth, and monkey fashion swung over the palace walls and into the wood.

The wood was cool and shining with gold and gems. In its midst was a marble palace, guarded by the ugliest of rakshasis. In the palace lay the form of a woman, scantily clad in rags and thinner than any living woman.

Hanuman watched as Ravana raised himself and approached the woman, who must surely be Sita. And he watched as the woman scorned him, and ignored his advances. The glitter in her eye betrayed her identity and Hanuman leapt up and down with glee. As Ravana left, the movement of the monkey caught Sita's eye and she looked at him with distrust. Probably Ravana in disguise, she thought tiredly, used to his tricks. But Hanuman whispered to her, and spoke reams of prayers for Rama, extolling his virtues. Sita was bemused and intrigued. She leant forward to hear more. Hanuman leapt down and spoke to Sita of Rama, presenting her with his

Opposite:
Ravana often appeared to Sita in disguise, and she was wary of anyone who approached – animal or man.

ring as a token of his continual concern for his dear wife. Sita knew then that Hanuman was friend, not foe, and she poured out stories of Rama, begging Hanuman to return at once to Rama in order that she could be rescued.

Hanuman took with him a jewel from her hair, and departed. His high spirits caused him to frolic on the way, and he could not resist

destroying a few of the trees around the palace. His activities drew attention, and he fought at the rakshasas who leapt up to meet him. He wounded or slayed all who approached him until at last he was caught by the enraged Ravana, who promised him instant death.

What could be worse for a monkey, he pronounced, than having his tail set on fire? And so it was ordered that Hanuman's tail should be set alight, in order that he should burn to certain death. Now Sita still had powers of her own, and she prayed then, in Rama's name, that the fire should not burn Hanuman, but rage on at the end of his tail, leaving him unscathed. And so it was that Hanuman was able to leap away across Lanka, touching his tail here and there, in order to burn most of that glittering city to the ground. And then, dousing his tail in the wide, curving ocean, he flew across the sea to Rama.

Rama greeted Hanuman which caused the monkey to squirm with delight. He recounted all that had happened in the forest of Lanka, and he told what he had done with his burning tail. The monkey host leapt and cheered for Hanuman for he had brought them great glory with his bravery, and his craftiness.

Sugriva issued orders that all the monkey host should march to the south, in order to lay siege to Lanka. They reached the shores of the sea at Mahendra, and there they made camp. Rama joined them, and the plan to release Sita was formed.

Rama's Bridge

VIBHISHANA WAS BROTHER TO RAVANA, and on the day that Rama set his camp on the shores of the sea, he was pacing around the palace at Lanka. He spoke angrily to his brother, pointing out that if a monkey could lay waste to half the city, what chance did they have against Rama and his monkey host? There could be nothing but death for all.

'From the day that Sita came,' said Vibhishana, 'there have been evil omens – the fire is ever obscured by smoke, serpents are found in kitchens, the milk of kine runs dry, wild beasts howl about the palace. Do restore Sita, lest we all suffer for thy sin.'

But Ravana dismissed his brother and said that Sita would be his. Vibhishana begged his brother to see reason, but Ravana had become blind in his obsession with Sita and he would not allow anything to

Opposite:
The siege of Lanka took many years to resolve, and it involved the near deaths of Rama and each of his men.

stand in his path. Vibhishana rose then, and heading over the sea with his four advisers, he said to Ravana, 'The fey refuse advice, as a man on the brink of death refuses medicine.'

And so it was that Vibhishana flew across the sea to Rama's camp and announced himself as an ally to the great Rama. A deal was struck.

The ocean was a formidable obstacle to the rescue of Sita, and Rama laid himself flat on the ground, begging the turbulent waters to open for him, in order that they could cross. After many days, if Rama had received no response, he would dry up the sea, and lay Varuna's home bare. Mighty storms erupted and across the world people trembled with fear. At last the ocean himself rose up and spoke to Rama, his head a mass of jewels pinning the great rivers Ganga and Sindhu to its peak. He spoke gently, his power simmering beneath a gentle exterior.

'Great Rama,' he said, 'you know that every element has its own qualities. Mine is this – to be fathomless and hard to cross. Neither for love nor fear can I stay the waters from their endless movement. But you can pass over me by way of a bridge, and I will suffer it and hold it firm.'

And so Rama was calmed, and plans were made to build a bridge. With the permission of the ocean, Rama dried up the waters of the north, causing the sea there to become a desert. Then he sent a shaft which caused that dry earth to bloom with woods and vines and flowers. The ocean presented to Rama and his men a fine monkey named Nala, Vishvakarma's son, and the monkey set in force a plan to build a bridge like none other. The host of monkeys began to follow his orders, and bit by bit, timber and rocks were thrust on to the sea until a mighty bridge was formed across its girth. And the monkey host and Rama passed over, in order that the siege of Lanka would begin.

The siege of Lanka was a story which took many years to resolve, and it involved the near deaths of Rama and each of his men. Garuda himself came down to heal their wounds, and the men fought on until, finally, Ravana was slain by Rama – with the Brahma weapon given to him by Agastya. Only this weapon had the force to take the life of the evil spirit, and the wind lay on the wings of this weapon, the sun and fire in its head, and in its mass the weight of Meru and Mandara. Rama held a mighty bow and the arrow was sent forth, where it met its mark on the breast of Ravana. The lord of the rakshasas was slain, and all of the gods poured bouquets of

Opposite:
Rama's greatest achievement had been accomplished and he ordered Sita to be brought to him at once.

blossoms, rainbows of happiness upon Rama and his men. Rama's greatest achievement – the reason for Vishnu ever having taken human form – had been accomplished.

Rama ordered Sita to be brought to him at once.

Sita's Second Trial

RAMA KNEW THAT SITA would not be accepted by his people, for she had lived in another man's house and they had no reason to believe that she was not stained by his touch. Rama greeted her coldly, and told her that he had no choice but to renounce her, as he must renounce everything that had been in contact with the greatest of evils. Sita, begged and pleaded – insisting upon her dedication to her glorious husband, and her continual and undying devotion.

'Oh king,' wept Sita, throwing herself at Rama's feet, 'why did you not renounce me when Hanuman came? I could have given up my life at that time, and you need not have laboured to find me, nor laid a burden on your friends. You are angry – like a common man you are seeing nothing in me but womanhood. I am the daughter of Janaka, Rama, and I am also daughter of the earth. I was born of earth and you do not know my true self.'

She turned then to Lakshman, and she said bravely, 'Build me a funeral pyre, for there is my only refuge. I will not live with an undeserved brand.'

And the fire was prepared.

The gods threw themselves upon the mercy of Rama, praying that he should relent. And an elderly Brahma came forward and spoke words that fell on the ears of the gods and all around them like jewels: 'Sita is Lakshmi and you are Vishnu and Krishna. No stain has touched Sita, and although she was tempted in every way, she did not even consider Ravana in her innermost heart. She is spotless.' The fire roared up in approval, and added, 'Take her back.'

And so Sita was returned to Rama's side, where he pledged his undying love for her. He explained then that this test had been for her own safety – that their followers would now respect her once again for she had been proved pure. Together they set out for Ayodhya, and home.

It had been fourteen long years since Rama had left Ayodhya, but the memory of him and his goodness had remained etched in the hearts of every citizen. When they arrived through the gates of the city, they were greeted with uproarious cheers, and celebrations like none other were

Opposite:
Sita sat beside her beloved husband, and as she drew herself nearer to him, he turned away from her, claiming that he must renounce her.

begun across the land. Bharata bowed to Sita and threw himself at Rama's feet. The kingdom was restored to Rama, and Bharata cried:

'Let the world behold you today, installed, like the radiant sun at midday. No one but you can bear the heavy burden of our empire. Sleep and rise to the sound of music and the tinkle of women's anklets. May you rule the people as long as the sun endures, and as far as the earth extends.'

'So it shall be,' said Rama.

Rama reigned happily in Ayodhya for ten thousand years, and then the day came when Sita conceived a child. Delighted by her news, he begged her to allow him to honour her with any wish, and she expressed a wish to visit the hermitages by the Ganges. Her wish was instantly granted and preparations were made for her travel. Lakshman was to accompany her, but before he left, he took counsel with his brother, the great Rama.

'I am concerned,' said Rama, 'that we know the feelings of our ministers and our people. We must call a conference to ensure that all is well in the kingdom.'

And so a conference was duly called and all of the counsellors and friends of Rama pledged their love for him, and their devotion. There was, however, one unhappiness which stained the otherwise perfect fabric of his rule.

'The people murmur that you have taken back Sita, although she was touched by Ravana and dwelt for many years in Lanka. For all that, they say, you still acknowledge her. That is the talk.' Rama's finest officer uttered these words and as he heard them, Rama's heart was chilled through and through. He sent for Lakshman and pronounced Sita's sorry fate.

'I am crushed by these slanders,' said Rama, 'for Sita was pronounced unstained by gods and fire and wind. But the censure of the people has pierced and this ill-fame can only bring me great disgrace. Take Sita tomorrow and leave her there, brother, and remove yourself now before I can change my mind.'

And so Sita and Lakshman travelled to the Ganges, armed with gifts for the hermits. When they arrived, Lakshman explained Rama's wish. Sita fell into a deep faint from which it took many minutes to recover. When she did, she spoke of her desolation, and her fear at being able to survive in the forest. She could not live there, she feared, and yet she would do so because her master had decreed it. She was faithful. She was unstained. She was prepared to prove it.

The Sons of Rama

THE WORLD ABOUT RAMA WAS CHANGING, and he was advised by the gods and by his counsellors that the age of Kali had begun. He continued to undertake acts of great kindness and goodness and his fine name sat comfortably on the tongues of subjects across the kingdom. But Rama was lonely. He longed for his great love Sita, and he longed for the day when she would be declared cleansed of all unrighteousness.

And that day came at last, when Rama prepared a horse sacrifice, and invited the hermit Valmiki to the ceremony. He was accompanied by two young boys, Kusha and Lava, and Rama was overjoyed to discover that these were the sons born of Sita, and that she was well and still living with the hermit Valmiki.

His two sons were born in his likeness, with voices as pure as a bird's. They were humble and kind, and when he offered them money for their performance to the people of the kingdom, they refused, saying that they had no need of money in the forest.

Sita was sent for, and Valmiki returned to his hermitage to fetch her. Sita followed Valmiki into a waiting assembly, where the hermit made a pronouncement: 'Oh Rama, Sita is pure and she did follow the path of righteousness but you renounced her because of the censure of your people. Do you now permit her to give testimony of her purity? These twin children are your sons, Rama, and I swear before you that if any sin can be found in Sita I will forgo the fruit of all austerities I have practised for many thousand years.'

And so Sita said quietly, 'I have never loved nor thought of anyone but Rama, even in my innermost heart. This is true. May the goddess of the earth be my protection. I pray now for Vasundhara to receive me.'

And the earth then thrust under the lovely Sita a throne so beautiful that each in the assembly gasped with pleasure. But the earth curled that throne around Sita and drew her back again into itself, home once again and part of the beginning and end of all things.

Rama screamed with despair and fought against the anger that threatened to engulf him. Rama carried on ruling then, for some time, but his heart was no longer in his country. Lakshman travelled to a hermitage and was eventually returned to Indra as part of Vishnu. Bharata no longer wished the kingdom, although Rama begged him to take it back, and eventually it was decreed that Kusha and Lava should rule the kingdom as two cities. But Ayodhya, as it once was, was no longer a kingdom to be ruled, for when Rama left he was followed by all of his people.

Rama joined together with his brothers then, and with the blessing and prayers of the gods and the entire population of his kingdom, he returned to Heaven as Vishnu, in his own form, with his brothers. All of the gods knelt down before him and they rejoiced.

Opposite:
Rama asked Lakshman to leave Sita in the forest by the banks of the Ganges, for she was to be submitted to a second trial.

And Brahma appointed places in the heavens for all who had come after Rama, and the animals were given their godly form. Each reached his heavenly state, and in Heaven, all was once again at peace.

On earth it was decreed that the *Ramayana* should be told far and wide. And to this day, it is.

✳ ✳ ✳

LEGENDS OF KRISHNA

rishna was originally the hero of the *Mahabharata*, a destructive, evil and immoral warrior who was known for his cunning and martial skills. Later, as Krishna became associated with Vishnu – his third human incarnation – his evil deeds were explained philosophically, and all manner of excuses was devised to explain his previous acts. The murders he had committed were to rid the earth of demons; his forays with women, and their subsequent search for him, have been explained in a metaphor of a worshipper seeking his god. Indeed, he came to represent the doctrine that devotion is a way to salvation. Krishna was a popular god, and the late addition of the *Bhagavadgita* to the *Mahabharata* presents him, alongside work and knowledge, as the means by which believers can be saved. But it is his childhood pranks that have come to characterize Krishna, and it is some of these which follow.

Krishna's Birth

THERE ONCE WAS A KING OF MATHURA, named Ugrasena, who had a beautiful wife. Now his wife was barren, a fact which dismayed them both and caused her to hold her head down in shame. One day, when walking in the wood, she lost her companions and found herself in the company of a demon who assumed her husband's form. Knowing not the difference between this man and the man who was her husband, she allowed him to lie with her and the product of this liaison was a long-awaited son, who they named Kansa.

When Kansa was a child he was cruel and a source of great sorrow to his family and his country. He shunned the religious teachings of the day and taunted his father for his devotion to Rama, the god of his race. His father could only reply, 'Rama is my lord, and the dispeller of my grief. If I do not worship him, how shall I cross over the sea of the world?'

The ruthless Kansa laughed heartily at what he considered to be his father's foolishness and immediately usurped his place on the throne. Immediately a proclamation was issued throughout the kingdom, forbidding men to worship Rama and commanding them to pay their devotions to Siva instead.

This arrogance and tyranny went on for many years, and every man and woman throughout the kingdom prayed for relief from the rule of this truly evil man. Finally, the Earth, assuming the form of a cow, went to Indra and complained. And so it was that Brahma listened to the pleas of the Earth and led them to Siva, and then Vishnu. Vishnu had in the past taken on the incarnation of man and they reminded him of that now, begging him to do so in order to afford the destruction of the seemingly invincible Kansa. Each of the gods and goddesses cheered Vishnu in this mission and promised to leave their heavenly homes in order that they could accompany him on earth. Vishnu arranged that Lakshman, Bharata and Sutraghna would accompany him and that Sita, who would take the name of Rukmini, would be his wife.

One day Kansa was carrying the great Vasudeva and his wife Devaki through the sky when a voice set out the following prophecy:

'Kansa, fool that you are, the eighth child of the damsel you are now driving shall take away your life!' And so Kansa drew his sword and was about to take the life of Devaki when Vasudeva intervened, and said:

Opposite: Vishnu was reincarnated in many forms, including, on one occasion, that of a fish. He was required to become human now, to see to the death of Kansa.

'Spare her life and I will deliver to you every child she brings forth.' Kansa laid down his sword, but he placed a guard with her who stayed by her side for her every living hour. And as child after child was given up to him and slain, he continued in his wretched mission.

But Devaki was a woman with a mind as quick as a tree squirrel, and although Kansa had been advised that the children he had destroyed were her own, this was not the case. The children that had been handed over to him were the children of Hiranyakasipu who had been lodged in the womb of Devaki in order that the cruel Kansa might be fooled. Vishnu said to the goddess Yoganindra, who brought the children from the nether regions:

'Go Yoganindra, go and by my command conduct successively six of their princes to be conceived by Devaki. When these shall have been put to death by Kansa, the seventh conception shall be formed of a portion of Sesha, who is part of me; and you shall transfer before the time of birth to Rohini, another wife of Vasudeva, who resides at Gokula. The report shall run that Devaki miscarries and I will myself become incarnate in her eighth conception; and you shall take a similar character as the embryo offspring of Yasoda, the wife of a herdsman called Nanda. In the night of the eighth of the dark half of the month Nabhas I shall be born, and you will be born on the ninth. Aided by my power, Vasudeva shall bear me to the bed of Yasoda, and you to the bed of Devaki. Kansa shall take you and hold you up to dash you against a stone, but you shall escape into the sky, where Indra shall meet and do homage to you through reverence of me.'

And so it was that when Devaki gave birth to her eighth son, Vasudeva took the child and hurried through the city. When he reached the River Yamuna, which he had to cross, the water rose only to his knees instead of seeking to drown him. And as he reached the house of Nanda, Yasoda had given birth to her child, which Vasudeva seized and, leaving Devaki's child in its place, returned to his wife's bed.

Soon after, the guard heard the cry of a newborn, and summoning himself from the depths of a good sleep, he called for Kansa, who immediately rushed into the home of Devaki and thrust the child against a stone. But as soon as this child touched the ground there was a cry as deep and angry as that of any rakshasa. It rose into the sky and grew into a huge figure with eight arms, each holding a great weapon. It laughed and said to Kansa, 'What avails it thee to have hurled me to the ground? He is born that shall kill thee, the mighty one amongst the gods.'

Kansa collected his ministers and gathered them round. He insisted that every man who was generous in gifts and sacrifices and prayers to the gods must be put to death so that no god shall have subsistence. He said then, 'I know now that the tool of my fate is still living. Let therefore active search be made for whatever young children there may be upon earth, and let every boy in whom there are signs of unusual vigour be slain without remorse.'

Soon after this Vasudeva and Devaki were released from their confinement, and quickly sought out Nanda, who was still unaware of the change in their children. Vasudeva had brought with him another of his children, by Rohini, who was Balarama, and placed him under the care of Nanda to be brought up as his own child. By this means, as Rama and Lakshman were inseparable companions in previous incarnations, Krishna and Balarama were intimately connected.

Nanda and his family had not been settled long at Gokula before efforts were made to destroy the infant Krishna. A female fiend called Putana, whose breast caused instant death when sucked, had taken the child in her arms and offered him a drink. The infant Krishna seized it with such fervour and sucked with such violence that the horrible fiend roared with pain and met with an instant death.

The birth of Krishna had caused great happiness, despite the evil decrees of Kansa, and throughout the land trees blossomed, flowers bloomed and there was music in the souls of all who lived on earth.

The Young Krishna

THE YOUNG KRISHNA was a very mischievous boy and his merry-making became legend throughout the land. One day, as a mere infant lying under the wagon of Nanda, he cried for his mother's breast, and impatient that she did not come to him at once, kicked the wagon over, to the great astonishment of all who witnessed this momentous occurrence.

When Krishna was but five months old, another fiend came in the form of a whirlwind to sweep him away, but at once he grew so heavy that his own surrogate mother could not hold him and had to lay him down. But when the storm became a cyclone, the infant allowed himself to be swept into the sky, and while all the people on the ground wept and bemoaned his sorry fate, he dashed the rakshasa down, killing him and ending the storm.

On another occasion, Krishna and Balarama played with the calves in the fields to such an extent that Yasoda became angry, and tied the errant Krishna to a heavy wooden mortar in which the corn from the farm was threshed. Krishna, trying to free himself, dragged it until it became wedged between two Arjuna trees and then, with a strong pull, uprooted the trees altogether. Again, the people of the surrounding farms were astonished because there had been no storm and yet the trees had fallen, and their roots were exposed. The land must be unlucky, they thought, and they moved away to Vrindavana.

Krishna's tricks were not only for the benefit of himself, for his companions were also defended by his fiery nature, trickery and quick thinking. One day, Brahma came and stole away the calves and the herd-boys, taking them to a cave among the mountains. Krishna quickly made another herd and another group of herd-boys in their likeness and placed them where he had found them. No one but Krishna knew their true identities and he waited impatiently for Brahma to come upon his trick. Now it was nearly a year later before Brahma remembered the herd and the children, and he found the boys and the calves asleep in the cave. But, when he went to Brindaban, he found the boys and the calves there too.

Brahma was puzzled, but he drew back in fear when Krishna, not content with his changelings, drew the herd-boys into the likeness of gods, with four arms and the shape of Brahma, Rudra and Indra. Krishna quickly returned the boys to their shape when he saw Brahma's fright, and Brahma restored them at once. When they awoke they knew nothing of the time that had passed, and Brahma was now in awe of the young Krishna, whose eager mind had caused such devilry.

There are many other tales related of Krishna's youth, for he liked nothing more than to stir a little trouble amongst the local gopis and cow-herds. There is a tale told of the day that Krishna stole the gopi's clothes. The girls had sought out a quiet place to bathe, and laying their clothes on the bank, they frolicked in the fresh water, their lotus eyes glowing with frivolity and the fervour of youth. They sang and played, and Krishna sat in the tree, watching his cows, but drawn to the happy songs of the gopis. Slipping down the bank, he snatched the clothes, and climbed up a kadamb tree which hugged the bank of the water hold.

When the gopis had completed their bath they returned to the banks to retrieve their clothes. They looked everywhere, raising their arms and brows in puzzlement at such a seemingly magical

occurrence. Until one of the gopis looked up and saw Krishna sitting in the tree, gently laying out the clothes of each girl. He was wearing a crown and yellow robes and she called out, 'There he is, Krishna, who steals our hearts and our clothes.'

The girls squealed, as all girls across the ages would have done, and plunged into the water to hide themselves. They prayed silently for Krishna to return their clothes but he would not hand them over.

'You must come and fetch them,' he said smartly, grinning from ear to ear.

'We shall tell on you,' said the girls, 'we shall tell your father and ours, and all our friends and you will be punished. Our husbands will protect our honour.'

But Krishna only laughed and said to them then, 'If you are bathing for me, then cast away your shame and come and take your clothes.'

The girls said to each other, 'We must respect him, for he knows our minds and our bodies. There is no shame with Krishna.' And they strolled then from the water, their arms at their sides but their heads lowered in deference to Krishna. At Krishna's encouragement they joined hands and waited for their clothes, which were duly presented. And so the gopis returned home, wiser in some small way that was unknown to them, and more attracted to and confused by the mischievous Krishna than ever.

Krishna and Kaliya

ONE DAY, THE COWHERDS SET OUT EARLY, wandering through the woods and along the banks of the river until they came to a place called Kaliya. There they drank of the river waters, and allowed their cows to drink as well. Suddenly there was blackness and each of the cow-herds and cows laid down, the rich and instant poison of the naga or water snake called Kaliya entering their veins and causing them to die a painful death. Kaliya had come there from Ramanaka Dwipa, where he had once made his home. Garuda, who was the enemy of all serpents, had gone to live at Ramanaka Dwipa and Kaliya had fled immediately, taking refuge in the only place that Garuda was unable to visit, due to an ancient curse. Kaliya was an evil, frothing snake, and for miles around his shimmering form, the river bubbled with the heat of his poison.

Now on this day, Krishna set out to seek the company of the cowherds and their cows, and he came upon their lifeless forms by the banks of the Jamna with some surprise. Krishna's powers were such

Opposite: Krishna stepped from Kaliya's head and set the serpent free. Kaliya gasped his gratefulness and prayed forgiveness for failing to recognize Krishna.

that it took only a glance to restore the life to their bodies once more, and this he did at once. But Krishna was unhappy about his friends being plagued and he leapt into the water. Now the great Kaliya rose with all one hundred and ten hoods spluttering his poison, and the cowherds wept and wrung their hands at his certain death in that water. But Balarama was calm.

'Krishna will not die,' he said calmly. 'He cannot be slain.'

Now Kaliya had wrapped himself around the body of Krishna, and he tightened his grip with all of his force. But Krishna outwitted him, and making himself so large, he caused the serpent to set him free. Again, Kaliya squeezed his bulk around the youth, but once again Krishna cast him aside by growing in size.

Then, Krishna suddenly leapt onto Kaliya's heads, and taking on the weight of the entire universe, he danced on the serpent's heads until Kaliya began to splutter, and then die. But there was silence and weeping, and the serpent's many wives came forward and begged Krishna to set their husband free. They laid themselves at his feet, and pledged eternal worship.

'Please release him,' they asked, 'or slay us with him. Please, Krishna, know that a serpent is venomous through nature not through will. Please pardon him.'

And so it was that Krishna stepped from Kaliya's head and set the serpent free. Kaliya gasped his gratefulness, and prayed forgiveness for failing to recognize the great Krishna, the Lord, earlier.

Krishna commanded Kaliya to return to Ramanaka Dwipa, but Kaliya lowered his head and explained that he could not return there for Garuda would make a meal of him at first sight. Krishna laughed, and pointed to the mark on Kaliya's head.

'Show him my mark, my friend,' he said to the serpent, 'for when Garuda sees that he will not touch you.'

From that day, the waters were cleared of poisons and the people rejoiced. Krishna was Lord.

Krishna and the Mountain

Opposite:
Krishna encouraged the gopas who were preparing to worship Indra to worship the mountain instead.

KRISHNA HAD LONG WISHED TO ANNOY INDRA – partly because he was mischievous by nature and partly because he envied the giver of rain for all the gifts he received from the people. And so it was on this day

that Krishna spoke to the gopas who were preparing to worship Indra, and he urged them instead to worship the mountain that had supplied their cattle with food, and their cattle that yielded them with milk. And following the wise Krishna's advice, the gopas presented the mountain Govarddhana with curds and milk and flesh, the finest offerings they had.

The crafty Krishna at once transformed himself, appearing on the summit of the mountain saying 'I am the mountain.' There he ate greedily of the offerings while in his own form, as Krishna, he worshipped the mountains with the gopas. Little did they know that Krisha wished only to divert the worship of Indra to himself and that he could appear both as the mountain and in his own form at will.

Now Indra was not pleased that his offerings had all but dried up, and pledging to punish the people, he sent down great floods and storms to destroy them and their cattle. An army of clouds swept across the skies and a rain like none had ever seen before was cast down.

'You told us to give up the worship of Indra,' chanted the gopas angrily. 'And now we will lose everything. You told us to worship the mountain and that we did. And so, great Krishna, bring that mountain to us now.'

And so it was that Krishna filled Govarddhana with all of the burning energy that filled his celestial body and he lifted it easily on the tip of one finger. Laying it over the people of Braj and their cows, he sheltered them from the rains and the floods until Indra gave up. Not even a drop of rain had fallen in Braj and Indra knew he had met the Primal Male.

The following day, as Balarama and Krishna lay lazily in the meadows, enjoying the sun and good fortune, Indra arrived and laid himself at Krishna's feet. Krishna was Lord.

Krishna and Radha

ONE DAY, AS THE COOL BREEZE wafted lazily at the ripples on the river, Krishna and Balarama lay in the grasses under the trees, playing on the flute and joking amongst themselves. As was usually the case they were soon joined by the lovely gopis, who had fallen under the spell of Krishna and who longed for his company. They came towards the music and took up his hands to dance. Now there were too many of these gopis to dance with Krishna and to hold his hands, but as they

danced he multiplied himself into as many forms as there were woman so that each woman believed she held the hand of the true Krishna.

It was on this same day that Krishna watched the gopis bathe in the Yamuna river after their dance. He loved them all, of course, but his particular favourite was Radha, the wife of Ayanagosha. Rhada's sister-in-law told her brother of his wife's misconduct with Krishna, and Radha was afraid that she would be murdered as she slept. But when she spoke her fears to Krishna he calmed her, and reassured her easily that when her husband came, he would transform himself into Kali, and instead of finding Radha with her lover, Ayanagosha would find her worshipping a goddess instead.

Krishna took Radha into his embrace, and as he did so, her husband passed. Looking up, he noticed his wife bowing down with Krishna, who appeared at once as the goddess Kali.

The love affair with Radha went on for many years. They walked together in the flowering woods, and she spent many hours worshipping his feet. When Radha made love to Krishna, they made the world, and their love-making was passionate and playful. After their love-making Krishna combed her hair and plaited and pinned it, a servant to his mistress, a

Opposite:
When Radha made love to Krishna, they made the world, and after their love-making, Krishna combed her hair, and walked with her in the moonlight.

servant to his great love. He helped her with her sari. Theirs was a true, divine love – personifying all that is good in the union of man and woman.

There are many more stories of Krishna, who continued his tricks and his love-making, eventually taking on some 16,000 wives, but that is the story of the *Mahabharata* and other tales.

✵   ✵   ✵

LEGENDS OF BUDDHA

uddha means 'Awakened One', or one who has found insight and enlightenment. There are many Buddhas, for he has had many incarnations, but the Buddha to which we refer today is the last incarnation of the great teacher Gautama Buddha, who was born in 563 BC as the son of Suddhodan, the king of Sakya. He is also called Siddhartha and Tathagata, or the one who walks the same path as his predecessors, his earlier incarnations. The myths of Buddha surround the privations and austerity he underwent to attain his enlightenment, and then, the miracles he was able to perform thereafter. When he had attained his awakening, Buddha passed away peacefully, surrounded by his disciples.

There were many stories of Buddha's birth, and it became an accepted belief that others could follow in his path – becoming Buddhist deities and being worshipped themselves. The following tales are some of the richest examples of Buddhist myth, which has, over the years, become embroidered to encompass philosophy of both Hindu and Buddhist religion.

The Life of Buddha

IT WAS IN THE FIFTH CENTURY, when Prince Gautama was born in Kapiavastu, the capital of Shakya. The Raja at this time was Suddhodana and he was married to the two daughters of the Raja of the neighbouring tribe, the Koiyans. There are many myths which set out the birth of Buddha, each subsequent version more splendid and divine. Queen Maya, wife of Suddhodana, recounts a dream in which she saw a white elephant lowered from heaven, and how the moon itself fell into her lap, a ball of pure, white light. And when the birth occurred, Buddha was thrust from her side, like the opening of the letter 'B'.

Now the young prince was born into great luxury, and he was cosseted and adored by the household on all sides. When he learned to walk there were arms outstretched in every direction, but the young prince shunned them all and took seven steps to the north, seven steps to the east, seven steps to the south and seven steps to the west, which signalled to all his spiritual conquest of the earth.

The prince was trained in every sport, becoming an expert in all kinds of martial skills. He was well versed in the arts, and he married, at a very early age, Yasodhara, who he won in a contest at the age of only sixteen. It was not long after this marriage that Yasodhara bore him a son, who he named Rahula.

Gautama lived the life of a normal Indian ruler, eating and drinking plenty, and finding great pleasure in the women the place offered. He had concubines and a chariot that took him far and wide. Although he was a wise man, he thought little about the world around him for it had been his oyster for as long as he could remember and he polished his own little pearl daily, enjoying what he saw in his reflection.

One day, as Gautama was out in his chariot with his respected confidante and charioteer Channa, he spied an old man shuffling along the earth and mumbling to himself. He leant heavily on his stick and clearly had some difficulty moving at all. Channa said wisely, 'Ah, that shall be the fate of all of us one day.'

Several days later Gautama was out once again with Channa, and he saw a man lying poor and ill in the gutter. He expressed some surprise that a man could be in such a state and asked Channa how this had happened.

Opposite:
Buddha's philosophy was worked out in his meditations, and all had become clear. He knew now that desire was the root of all evil.

Channa spoke wisely, 'Ah, this shall be the fate of all of us. Suffering comes to us all.'

It was on their third such trip that Gautama saw the body of a man who had recently died. He looked puzzled for such occurrences were not the common sight of princes. Any ugliness like illness and death had been swept from his sight until now.

Channa spoke wisely, 'Ah, this shall be the fate of us all.'

Now Gautama was deeply affected by his three experiences and it caused him to spend many long hours pondering his condition, and the fate that would eventually befall him – and them all. He found no pleasure in his food or drink. He left his women in peace and he decided that there was nothing lasting or true in his life. And so it was decided that he would leave his palaces and all the trappings of his life to live a life of meditation and solitude.

Later that night, by the glow of the silver moon, he ordered Channa to saddle his favourite horse Kanthaka, and they rode away from the palace, silently escaping from a life that Gautama now knew he could not live. The gods had smiled on him and his enlightenment, and they helped quiet the hooves of his horse so that the sound of their clatter on the flagstones would not waken his family. Without a whisper, the men left, Channa accompanying Gautama until they reached the edge of the forest. And there, stripping himself of his finery, the prince said good-bye to his dear companion and to his life. At the age of just twenty-nine, Gautama had left it all.

In the wilds of the Indian countryside, the prince lost himself to the world. For many years he sat in meditation. The gods sent him many temptations, including the daughters of Mara, the goddess of seduction, whose wiry bodies writhed and danced, offering him pleasures for which he had at one time hungered. But he resisted them all, for within Gautama was a new calm. He was on the verge of enlightenment.

Gautama fasted for long periods, until he realized the need for food. Reaching out, he plucked the fruit of the fig tree and in its leafy shade he achieved complete bodhi, or enlightenment.

His philosophy had been worked out in his meditations, and all had become clear. He knew now that desire was the root of evil, of anger and violence. He realized that desire made fools of man, chasing money and women and an afterlife. He realized that a person who cannot control desire goes through chains of existences – birth and then death and then birth again, over and over. This was a wheel which could be stopped; this was a chain which could be broken. By suppressing desire, links of the chain can be removed, and instead of there being rebirth after death, there would be the state of nirvana, where there could be no suffering, no more death, no more births.

And so the supreme Buddha took it upon himself to go back into the world, to preach his new wisdom. He could, then, have given himself over to nirvana but his calling drew him to spread the message, to reach out as a teacher to the people who needed deliverance from the unholy waste that their lives had become.

Buddha walked to Varanasi, where he dressed himself in yellow robes – a personification of the sunlight which flowed through his veins and fed his wisdom. He returned to Kapiavastu, and there he appeared to his own people, joined by his son Rahula. For the next forty-five years, Buddha wandered and preached. Animosity and anger were quietened by his gentle words – even the most ferocious of animals bowed to his touch.

Sumedha

To cease from all sin,
To get virtue,
To cleanse one's own heart –
This is the religion of the Buddhas.

IT IS POSSIBLE FOR ANY MAN to take the form of a Buddha, provided he can find enlightenment. There are, in the history of Buddhism, many cases of incarnations of the great Buddha himself, and we shall read of some of these very soon. There was, however, one case of a man becoming a Buddha-elect while the great Buddha lived. He was called Sumedha, and he lived in the great city of Amara.

Sumedha was a good man who was both wise and wealthy. He had been widely educated and his studies brought to his attention the unhappy lot that was the world around him. He was a Brahman and well-respected, and Sumedha knew he could count on the support of his peers and family in whatever he did. And so it was one day that Sumedha sat down and reflected on the misery that surrounded him. He too saw the unhappy chain of events that followed events – birth, death, rebirth and then death. And in between that unhappy chain fell the links of old age, disease, and for many, the poverty of the elderly.

So Sumedha took himself away then, far away to the Himalayas where he lived as a hermit in a house of leaves. He meditated and strove to attain enlightenment. A day came when the great Buddha would be passing near to Sumedha's hut, and the people of the mountain had come together to prepare a path for his feet. Sumedha joined eagerly in his work, and when the Buddha approached, he laid himself in the muddy rocks and leaves and sought a higher consciousness. And as he laid there, he realized that he could, at that moment, cast all his evil aside and enter into nirvana.

But the good Sumedha paused. How, he said to himself, how can I do this for myself. It would be better for all that I some day achieve complete omniscience and bring with me many people with the doctrines of Buddha.

There appeared at his side Dipankara, the Buddha who was known as One-who-overcame. Dipankara knelt beside Sumedha and rejoiced in his choice. The trees around them blossomed, and their leaves at once became lush. The earth became rich under his body, more fecund and fertile. From the clouds, the gods threw cascades of perfumed flowers.

'You have made the right choice,' said Dipankara. 'Go on and advance. Surely a Buddha thou shalt be, and give many others the chance to do the same.'

Sumedha returned then to the forest, where he practised carefully the conditions of a Buddha. They were perfection in alms, in keeping the precepts in renunciation, in good will and in indifference, and Sumedha learned them all. Beginning to fulfil the conditions of the quest he entered his hut and he stayed there. And then, one day, Sumedha died.

The forms by which he was reborn are countless, and in every one he stayed by his chosen path. Indeed, it has been said that there is not a particle of earth where the Buddha has not sacrificed his life for the sake of the creatures.

The Six-Tusked Elephant

THE JATAKA BOOK outlines the 550 rebirths of the Buddha-elect Sumedha, and this is just one. Once upon a time he was born as the son of an elephant chief, high in the Himalayas on the banks of a great lake. He was born into a royal herd, and they lived happily by the clear waters, enjoying the rich foods that grew on its shores, and finding shelter in the warm caves when the rains came each year. There was a great banyan tree, and the elephants lolled in its cool shade when the heat of the summer burned at their tender hides.

Opposite:
'You have made the right choice,' said Dipankara, and many men and women bent down to watch Sumedha rise, and then pass on his way to his own hut.

One steamy day, the Buddha-elect took shelter under the tree with his two wives, Chullasubhadda and Mahasubhadda. As the Buddha-elect reached up with his trunk to root out an insect, he accidentally sent down a shower of green leaves and flowers on his wife Mahasubhadda. On the other side, he had dislodged a spray of dry leaves and ants, and these struck Chullasubhadda smartly on the head causing her some pain, and even more jealousy. Later that day, another of the elephants presented the Buddha-elect with a lovely, fresh seven-sprayed lotus, and this he gave to Mahasubhadda. Chullasubhadda watched from behind the tree, her anger clouding what goodness remained within her.

That night Chullasubhadda laid under the tree and prayed that she might be reborn as the daughter of the king so that she could return as the queen of the king of Benares. She fell into a deep slumber, and her wicked wishes were granted. Chullasubhadda did not awake, and she returned as the favoured wife of the king of Benares. She remembered her wish to come back in this form and she remembered even more clearly the jealousy she had for the Buddha-elect's relationship with Mahasubhadda. She had returned for one reason alone – to destroy him – and that it what she set out to do.

The king of Benares returned to his chamber one evening to find his lovely wife in tears. He begged her to allow him to serve her in some way, and she spoke then of a wish that had been hers since she had been a child. With false innocence lighting her eyes, Chullasubhadda told the king that she had dreamed of a magnificent white elephant with six tusks. She longed for those tusks, she said, and if she could not have them she would surely die.

A hunter was chosen from the palace, and the queen explained to him where he would find the elephant. She promised him great riches and the hunter grudgingly agreed to go. He travelled deep into the Himalayas, far beyond the reaches of ordinary men, and he finally came upon the sweet waters of the lake, by which the herd of royal elephants rested. It was seven years since he had left the palace and he was weary from his travels. The great elephant was beautiful, and the hunter was suddenly saddened by the task ahead of him. Dressing himself in the yellow robes of a hermit who he had met on his travels, he slept for several hours in a hole he had dug near the herd.

When he awoke, he summoned up his courage. Preparing his poisoned arrow, he waited until the great elephant passed, and he shot

Opposite:
The king of Benares found his lovely wife in tears. She explained that she had dreamed of a magnificent white elephant with six tusks.

him straight through the head. Now the Buddha-elect would most certainly have sent this hunter to a sorry death if he had not seen his yellow robes. Intrigued by such poor behaviour on the part of a man of god, he knelt over the hunter and asked why he had performed an act of such violence.

The hunter, frightened by the presence of the elephant, confessed all. The Buddha-elect remembered his wife and he decided then that he would give in to her wishes. He allowed the hunter to saw at his tusks, an act which the poor tired traveller seemed unable to commit. He sawed at the tusks but with such ineffectual action that he caused the great elephant enormous pain and suffering, and filled his mouth with blood. And so it was that the great white elephant took the hunter's saw in his own hands and cut off his tusks himself. He presented them to the hunter, along with magic which would return him to the palace in seven days and seven hours.

As the hunter left, the great elephant laid down and died. That evening he was burned on the pyre by the others in his herd.

When the hunter returned to the queen, she leapt up and down with happiness at her conquest. She clutched the tusks to her breast and took to her bed in order to gloat. But as she looked at them there, saddled in her lap, she felt empty. And then, creeping into the empty hollow that had been her emotions, she felt despair and inconsolable grief. She remembered her life and her husband, and little by little the despair cracked her heart. The queen died.

When she was reborn, it was as Savatthi, a nun. One day she travelled to hear the doctrines of Buddha, and as she sat there, she realized that she had been married to him, and that he had once been the great white elephant. She swooned then, and burst into tears. But the great Buddha only smiled down on her, and when she told her story he only smiled again. Savatthi went on, it is said, to attain the sainthood, and it is her story that was responsible for many men following the great one's path.

Parinirvana

THE GREAT BUDDHA SPREAD THE WORD for forty-five years, and in the final year of his ministry, he suffered a grave illness. He knew then that his nirvana was approaching, and he prepared for the final release, called parinirvana for the great one. Buddha's illness came as he ate with a good smith called Chunda, who had prepared for him the most succulent pork.

It was this meat which brought on the final sickness, for it was tainted and it caused the great one to fall into a fever and a wretched faintness to which his whole body succumbed.

But Buddha felt no anger towards the Chunda, and indeed, as soon as he realized that his illness would, this time, be fatal, he called Chunda to his side.

'Chunda, your offering will bring a great reward. It is your doing which has brought on the attainment of nirvana, and for that I am thankful.'

Buddha made his pleasure clear to all his friends for he feared that Chunda would be blamed for his death when it was a time for rejoicing. Buddha lay himself down on a couch in a grove of sal-trees near Kushinagara. He sent a message to the princes of Malwa to come at once to his side, for he knew they would have a deep regret if they did not witness his final release, if they did not bid him farewell in person. Buddha's couch was soon surrounded by men of the highest order. There were kings and princes, priests and nobles, devas and brahmas of the ten thousand worlds, and they all gathered by his bed to see him pass. There was deep desolation and much weeping, which Buddha was unable to control.

Just before he was to take his last breath, Buddha was approached by a hostile Brahman of Kushinagara, who had not yet reached an understanding or acceptance of Buddha's teachings. Despite the cries of those around his bed to suppress the arrogant Brahman, Buddha was able to raise himself once more, in order to answer the young man's questions, and to argue the points to which he objected. In the end, there was a supreme silence, for the Brahman became a disciple and Buddha had the satisfaction of carrying his work, his teachings to his final rest.

He said to those around him, 'Now my friends I depart to nirvana, leaving you with my ordinances. Do not weep – seek the path to release and you may all reach nirvana. Work on your salvation,' he said quietly, and then he slipped into an unconsciousness which took from him his life.

The body of Buddha was wrapped in the finest cloths and laid in state for six days. And then it was burnt on a pyre in the coronation hall of the princes. The pyre ignited without match, for Buddha's body was ready for the final release, for parinirvana, and it was consumed at once. He left behind his teachings, and the goodness with which he had filled the world.

✳ ✳ ✳

TALES OF THE MAHABHARATA

he *Mahabharata* is one of the most magnificent epic poems of all time, and the longest in any language. The name *Mahabharata* probably applies to the Bharatas, who were descendants of King Bharata, the brother of Rama. The poem is unique in Indian literature, for it is driven mainly by the interplay of real people, rather than gods and demons, and it uses a plethora of very lively, dramatic and exciting personalities to present its message. Many believe that the entire philosophy of India is implicit in its romance, and its message is acted out in the great war waged between two ancient families – the Pandavas and the Kauravas, or Kurus.

The poem was finally edited by Krishna Dvaipayana, or Vyasa the Compiler, but since this character is, too, mythical, it is doubtful that his contribution is authentic. There have been many interpretations and many hands turning the text and indeed the pages of the *Mahabharata* over the centuries – and they have served not to clutter but to make clear the extraordinary vividness of the characterization, and the reasons why this has become the Indian national saga.

The Princes Learn to Shoot

BHISHMA WAS ROYAL GRANDFATHER to the houses of Pandava and Kuru, and he was eager for the princes of these royal houses to have a teacher who could train them in the dignified and royal use of arms. He had put out a search for such a teacher when it happened that the boys themselves were playing ball in the forests outside Hastinapura, when their ball rolled away from them and fell into a well. Although they struggled, and used all of their inventiveness, all efforts to reach it failed, and the ball was lost to them.

The boys sat glumly by the well, gazing with frustration at its walls when suddenly there was a movement from the corner of their eyes. There, thin and dark, sat a Brahman who seemed to be resting after his daily worship.

The boys eagerly surrounded him and begged him to recover their ball.

The Brahman smiled at their boyish jinks and teased them, for what offspring of a royal house could not shoot well enough to retrieve a ball? He promised to do so himself, for the price of a dinner. And then the Brahman threw his ring into the well and promised to bring that up too – using only a few blades of grass.

The boys surrounded the Brahman, intrigued. 'Why, that's magic,' said one of the boys. 'We could make you rich for life if you could do as you say.'

The Brahman was true to his word and selecting a piece of grass he threw it as if it were a sword, deep into the heart of the well and there it pierced the ball straight through. He immediately threw another blade, which pierced the first, and then another, which pierced the second, until soon he had a chain of grass with which to draw up the ball.

The boys had by now lost interest in their ball, but their fascination with the Brahman was growing by the moment.

'The ring,' they chorused. 'Show us how you can get the ring.'

And so it was that Drona, which was the name of that Brahman, took up his bow, which had been lying by his side, and choosing an arrow, and then carefully fitting it to the bow, he shot it into the well. Within seconds it had returned, bearing with it the ring. He handed it to the boys who whooped and hollered with glee.

Opposite:
There, thin and dark, sat a Brahman who seemed to be resting after his daily worship.

They surrounded Drona again, begging him to allow them to help him, to offer him some gift. Drona grew silent and then with great effort he spoke, carefully choosing his words.

'There is something you can do,' he said quietly. 'You can tell Bhishma your guardian that Drona is here.'

The boys trooped home again and recounted their adventure to Bhishma. Their guardian was at once struck by the good fortune of this visit for he did indeed know of Drona and he would, it seemed, be the perfect teacher for these unruly boys. Bhishma had known Drona as the son of the great sage Gharadwaja, whose ashrama in the mountains had been a centre of higher learning. Many illustrious students had attended as scholars, and most of these had befriended Drona who had been, even then, gifted with divine weapons and the knowledge of how to use them.

Drona had fallen upon hard times when he had pledged his allegiance to Drupada, now king of the Panchalas. Drupada and Drona had been fast friends as scholars, but as regent, Drupada scorned their ancient friendship and set the poor Brahman in the position of a beggar. Hurt by his friend's actions, Drona had left to pursue his studies, and his first task was to find the best pupils to which he could apply his knowledge.

Bhishma did not ask what purpose Drona had for these good pupils, and it was with warmth and genuine delight that he welcomed Drona to his household.

'String your bow, Drona,' he said, 'and you may make the princes of my house accomplished in the use of arms. What we have is yours. Our house is at your disposal.'

The first morning of instruction found Drona lying the boys flat on their backs. He asked them then to promise that when they became skilled in the use of arms they would carry out for him a purpose that he had borne in mind. Ever eager, Arjuna, the third of the Pandavas, jumped up and promised that whatever that purpose might be, he was prepared to accomplish it. Drona drew Arjuna to him and the two men embraced. From that time there would be a special closeness between teacher and student.

The princes came from all the neighbouring kingdoms to learn of Drona and all the Kurus and the Pandavas and the sons of the great nobles were his pupils. There was, among them, a shy and wild-looking boy called Karna who was by reputation the son of a royal charioteer. Arjuna and Karna became rivals, each seeking to outdo the other with his skill and accuracy.

Opposite:
Drona's pupils were soon accomplished in the dignified use of arms, and each sought to outdo the other with his skill and accuracy.

At this time, Arjuna was becoming well versed in the vocabulary of arms. One night while eating, the lantern blew out and he realized that he could still continue to eat in the darkness. It set his mind on to the thought that it would certainly be possible to shoot in darkness, for it surely was habit as much as putting food to one's mouth. Drona applauded Arjuna's crafty mind and declared him to have no equal.

Another of those who travelled to Drona to become a pupil was a low-caste prince known as Ekalavya. Drona refused to take him on because of his caste, and Ekalavya retired to the forest where he made an image of Drona from the earth, which he worshipped and revered as the man himself. He practised often in the forest and soon became so fine a shot that his activities were drawn to the attention of Drona and his pupils.

Drona sought him out and when Ekalavya saw him coming, he fell to the ground. 'Please, Drona,' he cried, 'I am your pupil, struggling here in the woods to learn the skills of military science.'

Drona looked down on the boy. 'If you are,' he said, 'give me my fee.'

Ekalavya leapt to his feet. 'Master, just name your fee and you shall have it. There is nothing I would not do for you.' His face was broken by a wide smile.

'If you mean it,' said Drona coolly, 'cut off your thumb.'

Ekalavya allowed no reaction to cross his proud face and he did as his master bid at once. He laid the thumb of his left hand at the feet of Drona and held up his head.

Drona turned with Arjuna and left, and as Ekalavya bent to collect his bow he realized that he could no longer hold it. His lightness of touch was gone.

And so it was by these means, and others like them that Drona ensured the supremacy of the royal princes, who had, now, no rivals in the use of arms. Each had a speciality and they were all capable of fighting with resourcefulness, strength and perseverance.

The Princes' Trial

DRONA'S PUPILS HAD NOW COME to the end of their education, and Drona applied to Dhritarashtra the king to hold a tournament in which they could exhibit their skill. Preparations began at once for the great event, and a hall was built for the queens and their ladies.

When the day arrived, the king took his place, surrounded by his ministers and minions, and by Bhishma and the early tutors of the princes. And then Gandharai, the mother of Duryodhana, and Kunti, the mother of the Pandavas, entered the area, beautifully dressed and bejewelled as befitted their stature. Last came Drona, who entered the lists dressed in white, as pure as the heart of Vishnu. Beside him walked his son, Ashvathaman, who held himself with great pride and authority.

In came the princes to a procession, led by Yudhishthira, and there began the most incredible display of expertise seen by any one of the noble spectators of that tournament. Arrow after arrow flew, never missing its mark. Horses pulled chariots and there was much vaulting and careering, but never did the princes lose control or exhibit anything other than the greatest of skill and precision. The princes fought together, and exhibited alone. Their mastery left none in any doubt that he was witnessing the finest example of marksmanship in the land. And then entered Arjuna, and Kunti gave a sigh of delight. Her son was even superior to his splendid cousins and he shot arrows that became water, and then fire, and then mountains, and then an arrow that made them all disappear. He fought with sword, and mace, and then pole and on the breast of his chariot. He met every mark with perfect precision. Here was a champion, and the audience hardly dared expel breath at this show of proficiency.

But the respectful silence that had fallen over the crowd was disturbed by a rustling in the corner. And then a great noise was heard in the direction of the gate. Into the centre of the ring came none other than Karna, grown to manhood and splendid in his arms. Far from the prying eyes of her neighbours, Kunti swooned and shivered with fear. Karna was none other than the son she had given up long ago, the son of the sun itself. He shone as brightly as any summer ray, his good looks matched by his eagerness to fight. He was tall and strong, and his presence caused the crowd to gasp with admiration.

Karna walked towards Arjuna and spoke quietly. 'Oh prince,' he said, 'I have a wish that we should engage in single combat.'

Arjuna could hardly hold back the spittle that multiplied on his tongue. He spluttered and then whispered angrily to Karna, 'The day will come when I will kill you.'

'That is yes, then?' shouted Karna. 'Today I will strike off your head before our master himself.'

The two men stood facing one another, antipathy growing between them like the strongest of armour. They moved into position for single combat, but just as they did so there was a cry from the master of ceremonies. Quietly he made his way across the field and drew the warriors to one side. Until Karna could show noble lineage, he was not by law able to fight with the sons of kings. Princes could not fight with men of inferior birth.

Karna's fury was tangible, but just as he turned to the master he was rewarded by a cry from Duryodhana, who was eager to see Arjuna defeated. 'I'll install him as king of Anga!' he shouted. 'And Arjuna can fight him on the morrow.'

Priests appeared at once, and a throne was brought for Karna, who beamed when he saw his old father Adhiratha, the ancient charioteer. He embraced his son, pride at his position as king causing him to weep with joy. There was some sniggering amongst the crowd, for how could a king have such a lowly father? But before anyone could speak, Duryodhana leapt forward once again, having pledged eternal support and friendship to Karna.

'We do not know the lineage of all heroes,' he shouted to the crowd. 'Who asks for the source of a river?' And to the cheers of the gathering, he wrapped his arms around Karna's shoulders and helped his aged father to a seat.

The princes and Karna left together. Kunti stared quietly at her sons – princes and now a king. She said nothing and watched them leave, undefeated and grand in every sense. Kunti looked then to the sun ... and smiled.

Opposite:
There began the most incredible display of expertise seen by any one of the noble spectators of the tournament.

The Bride of the Pandavas

MANY EVENTS HAD BEFALLEN THE PANDAVAS since the day of the tournament and they had gone into hiding, disguised as Brahmans in the town of Ekachakra. There came to visit them one day an old and fast friend who told them that Drupada, king of the Panchalas, was planning a swayamvara for his daughter Draupadi. They spoke at length about the virtues of the fair princess, and soon the time came for their friend to part.

The princes were silent when their guest had gone and Kunti mourned for her sons who had been cast out. She smiled brightly at them and said, 'Perhaps it is time to depart from Ekachakra – I for one am glad to renew our wanderings.'

The spirits of the princes were lifted at once, and the following day they set off, thanking their gentle host for all his many kindnesses. Before they knew it, they were on the road to Kampilya, the capital of Drupada. As they travelled, they met up with other Brahmans going along the same road in order to witness the great spectacle that was about to take place.

Alone in his castle, Drupada perused the swayamvara that he was about to hold and he wondered aloud at the choice of suitors. He had held for many years a secret wish that Arjuna should wed Draupadi, a wish that he had kept close to his breast over the last years. Arjuna's mastery of the bow was fresh in his memory as he formed the instrument that would be required to shoot an arrow through a ring suspended at great height. It would not be easy to win his princess. In fact, thought Drupada, there was likely only one man who could do it.

The day of the swayamvara dawned bright and clear and the crowds poured in from adjoining kingdoms and lands. Duryodhana came with his dear friend Karna, and the Pandavas arrived in disguise, taking the form of Brahmans once again and living in the hut of a humble potter.

As the festivities began, the lovely Draupadi entered the arena, her stunning robes and jewellery matched only by her shimmering beauty.

Opposite:
The lovely Draupadi entered the arena, her stunning robes and jewellery matched only by her shimmering beauty.

She held in her hands a wreath and she stood quietly while her twin brother Dhrishtadyumna stepped forward, his booming voice carrying across the crowds, 'Today you are assembled here for one purpose. He who can use this bow' – he gestured down and then up – 'to shoot five arrows through that ring, having birth, good looks and breeding, shall take today my sister for his bride.'

A cheer went up among the crowd and the first name on the list was called forward.

Many men reached for that sturdy bow, but none was able even to string it. Karna, sensing the embarrassment of his peers, stood and moved toward the weapon, his head held high, his good looks glowing in the morning sunlight. But as Draupadi caught sight of Karna, her lips curled and she called out with great disdain, 'I will not be married to the son of a charioteer.'

Karna managed a smile and shrugging his shoulders, returned to the crowd. There appeared, then, a movement from its masses, and the gathering parted to let through the strong but bedraggled form of a Brahman. Some of the Brahmans in the crowd cheered aloud as a symbol of sovereignty. Others shook their heads at what was bound to be a disgrace for Brahmans altogether.

Arjuna walked forward in his Brahman disguise and he lifted the bow with ease. Stopping to say a quiet prayer he walked slowly round the weapon until as quick as a flash he drew it up and sent five arrows flying straight through the ring. The cheering was uproarious. Brahman's across the crowd waved their scarves and flowers were sent flying from each direction. The other Pandavas kept down their heads, fearing that Arjuna's victory would draw attention to them all. So far no one had noticed that the Brahman was none other than Arjuna, and Draupadi brought forward a white robe and garland of marriage, which she placed eagerly about his neck.

'I take you as my lord,' she said happily.

Suddenly a roar went up from the crowds, and coming towards them were the other suitors, angered that a Brahman should steal what they thought was rightfully theirs. A great fight broke out and Arjuna and his brother Bhima stood firmly against the masses, proving themselves once again to be excellent fighters. Bhima tore out a tree by its roots and used it to fend off the crowds, a trick he had learned at the hand of Drona. The crowd gasped once again in delight. It was not often that they were treated to such a display.

In the royal gallery, a prince by the name of Krishna stood up.

'Look,' he shouted, pointing out Arjuna and Bhima to his brother, 'I would swear as my name is Krishna that those are the Pandavas.' He watched silently and said no more, waiting for his moment.

On the field the fighting continued until, finally, after much bloodshed, Arjuna was able to extract himself with his brothers and his new bride and return to the home of the potter. Unknown to the brothers, Draupadi's twin brother had been sent by Drupada to hide in next room in order to find out whether it was indeed Arjuna who had strung that bow and sent the arrows so smoothly through their ring.

Kunti greeted the princess warmly and welcomed her to the family, allowing her the honour of cooking for them on that first night. Nearby Dhrishtadyumna lay waiting, his ears pricked for news. If his sister was to marry a Pandava, whatever fate would befall her?

❋   ❋   ❋

LEGENDS OF SHIVA

hiva is a Sanskrit word meaning 'auspicious one', and although he is worshipped as profoundly, he is a more remote god than Vishnu. Shiva is the Moon-god and lord of the mountains, with the moon in his hair from which flows Ganga, the sacred River Ganges. He is also god of the yogis, the father of Brahmans who knows and recites the Vedas. Shiva has many other incarnations and as the centuries have passed he has taken on different roles and forms for each new generation of worshippers. Doctrines about Shiva may have merged roles that were once assigned to various earlier gods, for his personifications seem so diverse. Shiva is considered to be both destroyer and restorer.

But the stories which surround Shiva are fascinating and full of allegorical messages. Shiva's dance is one of the most memorable representations in literature – a demon-like god who dances to show the source of all movement in the universe, and most of all his five acts: creation, preservation, destruction, embodiment and release. The stories that follow present a portrait of one of the two great gods of post-Vedic Hinduism, and the very real message they depict.

Shiva

THE THIRD OF THE HINDU TRIAD, Shiva was first known as the destroyer, for his work would balance that of the triumvirate, the two other sides of which were Vishnu the preserver and Brahma the creator. In his early incarnations, he is said to be Rudra, who appears in the *Vedas*, and his story as Rudra of the *Mahabharata* and many of the other great Hindu works is this:

On the day that Rudra was born, the earth was lit from within. Into the world came a boy, but he entered crying, and Prajapati said to him, 'Why do you weep when you have been born after toil?'

The boy said then, 'My evil has not been cleansed from me and I have not been given a name. Give one to me now,' he begged. And so Prajapati pronounced: 'Thou art Rudra.'

Now Rudra, or Shiva as he came to be known, was created by Brahma in order to create the world, and in order for him to do so, he required a wife. A goddess is a god's other half, and both of these halves must work together to create the energy necessary for divine acts. Brahma realized that Shiva would need a partner, and so it was arranged that he would have one.

Shiva and Sati

THERE ONCE WAS A CHIEF OF GODS by the name of Daksha. He was married to Prasuti, the daughter of Manu, and she conceived and bore him sixteen daughters. The youngest of these daughters was Sati, and it was she who would become the wife of the supreme Shiva.

Now Daksha was not happy about marrying his youngest daughter to Shiva, for it had come to his notice, once before at a festival, that he had not offered homage to Daksha. Being a man of small mind, Daksha had held this against him as a grudge, and had pronounced a curse upon Shiva that he would receive none of the offerings made to the gods. A wandering Brahman, however, had been witness to the curse, and had laid down a contrary curse in order that Daksha should have nothing in his life but the wastage of material goods and pleasures.

As Sati grew, she knew her future was with Shiva, and she quietly worshipped him. When she reached an age at which it was suitable to marry, Sati was given a swayamvara, or 'own-choice', to

Opposite:
Daksha was married to Prasuti, the daughter of Manu, and she conceived and bore him sixteen daughters – the youngest of whom was Sati.

which he invited gods, princes and men of all great ranks from around the country. Sati was handed a wreath and with great excitement, she entered the assembly of men, eagerly searching the crowds for Shiva.

Now Shiva had not been invited to the swayamvara, for Daksha wanted nothing more to do with him, but he had not counted on the deep feelings of his youngest daughter. Her despair crumpled her young face and as she stared out into the crowd she felt nothing but love for Shiva. Calling out his name, she threw her wreath, and made to retreat. But there, in the middle of the court, her prayer had been answered. Summoned by her heart-felt cry, Shiva had responded and he stood there now, her wreath around his noble neck.

Daksha was bound by honour to marry his daughter to Shiva, and it was with great bitterness that he said, 'Though unwilling I will give my daughter to this impure and proud abolisher of rites and demolisher of barriers, like the word of a Veda to a Sudra.'

The happy couple travelled at once to Shiva's home in Kailas. His palace was exquisite, with every luxury and catered for by all manner of servants and women. But Shiva was not content with the good things alone, and he spent many hours wandering the hills surrounding Kailas, dressed in the robes of a beggar, his bedraggled wife Sati at his side. But Sati and Shiva were, one day, dressed well, and out to seek some air in their chariot when Sati received Daksha's invitation to take part in a great sacrifice that he was about to make.

Because of the enmity between the two men, Shiva had not been invited. Sati was broken hearted when Shiva explained to her, 'The former practice of the gods has been that in all sacrifices no portion should be divided to me. By custom, established by the earliest arrangement, the gods lawfully allot me no share in the sacrifice.'

But Sati was determined to attend the sacrifice, and although Shiva tried to dissuade her, she set off for her father's home. She was received there without honour, for she rode on the back of Shiva's bull and she wore the dress of a beggar. Daksha immediately became the victim of her tongue, for she gave him a sharp redressing for his treatment of Shiva the good. But in the middle of her speech, her father broke in, calling Shiva nothing more than a 'goblin', a 'beggar' and an 'ashman'. Sati, who had found great peace with her husband, announced, 'Shiva is friend to all, Father. No one but you speaks ill of him. All that you are saying his people know, and yet they love those qualities in him for he is a man of peace and goodness.'

Sati paused now, and thought for a moment. Then, with a fire that glinted from her eyes she made a decision and spoke once more: 'A wife, when her lord is reviled, if she cannot slay the evil speakers, must leave the place and close her ears until she hears no more. Or if she has the power, she must take her own life, and this I will do, for I am deeply shamed to have a body that was once a part of your own.'

And so it was that Sati released the fire within her and fell at the feet of her father. Sati was dead.

The news of his dear wife's death reached Shiva within moments, and he tore at his hair with a frenzy of despair and fury. His eyes glowed red and then gold, and with all the energy he could summon he called forth a demon as terrible as there ever was. This demon kissed the feet of Shiva and pledged to undertake any request he might have.

Shiva spat out the words, hardly able to control his great anger, 'Lead my army against Daksha and take care that his sacrifice is destroyed.'

And so the demon flew at once to the assembly, and with Shiva's ganas, he broke the vessels, polluted the offerings, insulted the holymen and then, with one fell swoop, cut off the head of Daksha and tainted the guests with smears of his fresh blood. Then the demon returned to Shiva at Kailas but he was deep in meditation and could not be reached. Brahma prayed to him to pardon Daksha, and to ease the suffering of the injured gods and rishis who had been in attendance at the sacrifice.

So Shiva lifted himself from his deep dreams and proceeded to Daksha's home, where he permitted his dead wife's father the head of a goat which would allow him to live. Shiva was invited then to the sacrifice, and allowed to partake of the offerings. Daksha looked upon him with reverence, and as he did so, Vishnu appeared on the back of Garuda. He spoke then to Daksha with a gentleness that touched the hearts of all who saw him:

'Only the unlearned deem myself and Shiva indistinct. He and I and Brahma are as one. We have different names for we are creation, preservation and destruction, but we three make up one as a whole. We are the tribune self. We pervade all creatures. The wise therefore regard all others as themselves.'

And then, as the crowds cheered and saluted these most wise and noble gods, the three parts of the universe left and went their separate ways — Shiva to his garden, where he fell once more into the solace of his dreams.

Shiva's Dance

Arise Oh my beloved wife
I am thy husband Shiva-ji
Open thy eyes and look at me!
With thee I can create all things
Without thee I am powerless
I am a corpse, I cannot act
Forsake me not, come back to me!
Oh, let me see thy smile again
Say something sweet into my ear
Dost thou not see me weeping here?
Thy words will be unto my heart
Like summer rain on thirsting land
You used to greet me when we met
With joy and with a smiling face
Why art thou still and without voice?
Cans't thou not hear how I lament?
Oh Mother of the Universe,
Oh Mistress of my very soul, arise!
My beautiful and loving wife,
My faithful spouse, return to me!

SHIVA DANCES TO MARK CHANGE, to show the transition from one stage to another. When the body of his wife Sita was burned, he took her ashes and began to dance, whirling in a flurry of movement that tore at the air around him and sent up a torrid flash of colour. He held a drum as he danced, turning and circling until the entire world began to shake. He moved swiftly, and whirled and turned around the world seven times before he was caught and stopped. The gods were frightened by the violence of his sorrow and they promised then to restore Sita to him. She was returned to him several days later as Uma, or mother. Shiva himself had become Nataraja, or the king of the dance.

There are many other legends of Shiva's dance, and another is recounted here. Shiva heard word that there were, in the forests of Taragam, ten thousand rishis who had become heretics who taught a false religion. Shiva was determined that they should know the truth, and he summoned his brother Vishnu to take the form of a beautiful woman and to accompany him to the forest. Shiva himself dressed as a yogi, and he wore his customary rags and ashes. As they entered the forests, they were immediately set upon by the wild wives of the rishis, women whose lust for men caused them to throw themselves at Shiva in his

Opposite:
Sita was returned to him several days later as Uma, or mother. Shiva himself became Nataraja, or the king of the dance.

yogi disguise. The rishis themselves were attracted to Vishnu as well, and so there was pandemonium, as the unholy men and women crowded round the two visitors, clawing at them.

And then there was silence. For all at once it had occurred to the people of Taragam forest that things were not quite right, and gathering together they threw curses at the visitors. A sacrificial fire was built, and then from it was called a mighty tiger, who flung himself upon Shiva in order to eat him whole. Shiva plucked at the tiger and set him to one side, removing his skin whole and causing the heretics to gasp. He wrapped the skin around himself like a shawl, and then, as the rishis produced a serpent more terrible than even Kaliya, he wound it round his neck and began to move. A malevolent dwarf goblin took the centre of the room, swinging his great club with one purpose alone. Shiva dealt with him easily, and with one foot pressed upon its back he began to twirl, and to execute an angry dance.

The heavens opened and the gods lined the walls, anxious to witness the splendid fervour of Shiva in action. The rishis watched in an amazement that fed their diminished belief so that they threw themselves down before Shiva and proclaimed him their most glorious god.

Shiva's dance lived on in their memories and Shiva and his dance were invoked on more than one occasion by every one who had borne witness. Some believe that when devotion is fading, Shiva will appear and dance. For when the faithless see this dance there can be nothing but conviction in their hearts.

✸   ✸   ✸

Opposite:
Shiva wrapped the serpent around his neck, and with one foot raised, he began to execute an angry dance.

MISCELLANEOUS MYTHS

here are a huge number of fascinating fables, fairy tales, myths and legends which form the backbone of Indian philosophy explaining ideology that was often complex. Some of these stories had their root in the epics, and in religious works. And later Hindu religious literature calls upon a host of characters and creatures introduced in the *Vedas*, the *Brahamanas*, the *Puranas* and some of the lesser known epics to draw attention to their message, and to exemplify the points they wish to put forth. Many of these stories, plucked from a larger original, and bejewelled with the words of generations, can now stand alone, as individual tales, and lessons. It is often these shorter parables that provide the guidelines for living, which allow new gods to force their way into the pantheon, and which represent some of the most compelling literature of any country in the world. There are thousands of variations of each of these tales, for most of them were not committed to writing for many centuries after their composition – the oral tradition keeping them burning in the consciousness, memories and perceptions of the culture.

The Birth of Ganga

O saint, I yearn
The three-pathed Ganga's tale to learn.
Thus urged, the saint recounted both
The birth of Ganga and her growth:

THERE ONCE WAS A KING OF AYODHYA named Sagara who was anxious to have a son. He provided the saint Bhrigu many penances over the years and finally, the saint was happy to announce that Sagara's worship would be rewarded.

'You shall have a glorious name, and one of your queens shall bear a son to maintain your race and to become your heir. And of the other, there shall be some sixty thousand born to you,' said the saint.

Now the wives of Sagara were most anxious to know which of them would have one son and which would have the vast number predicted. Kesini wished for one child, while Sumati was happy to have sixty thousand. Time passed and Kesini gave birth to a son called Ansuman, who became the heir. And Sumati, the younger of the two wives, gave birth to a gourd whose rind broke to reveal sixty thousand babies.

About this time King Sagara decided to make a horse sacrifice in order to become the reigning Indra, or king of the gods. As the preparations were being made, Ansuman was given the task of following the horse set apart for the sacrifice for according to ritual it was to be set free and allowed to wander for a whole year wherever it would.

Now the present Indra began to fear that such a sacrifice would rid him of his crown, and veiling himself as a demon, he arrived on the appointed day and drove the horse away. King Sagara called at once for his sons to search for the stolen horse, begging them to pursue the demon that had caused it to escape.

And so the sons of Sagara began their search, each digging one league in depth towards the centre of the earth. But still they could not see the horse. The gods were alarmed by the digging of the earth, and they went to Brahma to advise him of the destruction. Brahma was calm, for the earth was protected by Vishnu, and the sons of Sagara would be turned to ashes for their handiwork. The gods returned home to wait for retribution, and as they did so, the sons dug on.

Sixty thousand leagues were dug into the earth without any sight of the horse, and the princes returned to their father requesting

Opposite:
And so the sons of Sagara set out to search for the stolen horse, and the demon that had caused it to escape.

guidance. Sagara bid them to dig on, and to continue their search until the horse was found. The sons began to dig once again until there before them stood Vishnu. Thinking that the glitter in his eyes was one of welcome, the sons rushed forward to greet him. Moments later they were but ashes.

King Sagara waited disconsolately for news of his sons, but none arrived. Soon he sent his grandson Ansuman to look for them, but he learned nothing of their fate. Ansuman travelled widely, searching for news but he remained unrewarded, until the day when he reached the very spot of their deaths. Ansuman fell to the ground with dismay when he realized the significance of the ashes. As his tears hit the ashes, his uncle Garuda appeared and offered him consolation, holding carefully the harness of the horse that had been lost so long ago.

Prince Ansuman returned to the kingdom. Garuda had given him some advice and he thought carefully about it before he approached his grandfather.

'Garuda has said,' whispered Ansuman, 'that if Ganga would turn her stream below, her waves would wash the ashes of the two princes pure again, and the sixty thousand leagues would be restored while you took Indra's place in the heavens.'

The king thought carefully, thoughts which carried over thirty thousand long years. He had no idea how to induce Ganga to come down from the heavens, and at last he went there himself. After his death, the task became his grandson's and then that grandson's son's. And so it was finally given to Bhagirath to accomplish the work, for he had no son. After many years of austerity, Brahma came to Bhagirath and said to him then:

'You have been blessed, for your austerities have won my grace. What can I do to help you?'

Bhagirath replied, 'I would like Ganga to be let loose with her holy wave, so that the ashes of the heroes shall be washed pure and my kinsmen, Sagara's sons, shall ascend to heavenly bliss for the rest of their days. And please,' he added, 'I wish for a son so that my house shall not end here with me.'

And Brahma said to him then, 'If you pray for this, so it shall be.' Bhagirath stayed in his position of prayer for one year, even as Brahma returned to heaven. Shiva, pleased with the devotion, promised to sustain the shock of the waters. Ganga, however, was not pleased with the command that she descend to earth.

Ganga threatened to wash Bhagirath into hell with her waters and as she made for the earth she was caught by the wily Shiva, who held on to the coils of her hair until her anger abated. Then she fell into the Vindu lake, from which came the seven sacred streams of India. One branch of the stream followed Bhagirath wherever he went. At last Bhagirath reached the ocean and ascended to the depths where Sagara's sons were lying. Ganga followed until her waters touched the ashes. Suddenly their spirits rose and like glittering birds they entered heaven in a burst of light.

The faith in this legend has not died. Indeed, one of the most common places of pilgrimage in India is Sagara Island, where the river Ganges and the ocean meet. Sagara's sons and his son's sons rank high in heaven and will forever more.

The Elephant and the Crocodile

THERE ONCE WAS A ROYAL ELEPHANT who made his home with a royal herd on the banks of Triple Peak. They were happy here, for there was plentiful food and drink, and he had many wives who held him dear to their hearts. The day arrived when the royal elephant felt hot and fevered by the oppressive weather, and struggling towards an unknown lake, he plunged in and drank thirstily, stopping to cool his brow with a rush of water from his trunk.

As he reached into the water again to draw water for his wives and his children, he was attacked by a wrathful crocodile whose weight and size made him a very fearful opponent.

Crocodile and elephant fought together in the lake until the old elephant, weakened by the struggle and by his earlier fever, began to fade. His wives and children watched helplessly from the banks, calling out in terror and crying for help. And then, all at once, the elephant closed his eyes and began to pray. He prayed with such devotion to Vishnu, the supreme being, that his ardour was at once rewarded and Vishnu himself appeared on the back of Garuda. With ease he lifted the crocodile from the lake and cut its throat, throwing it back so that its blood stained the waters.

The royal elephant was saved. Now this was not just devotion that had caused Vishnu to come to the elephant's rescue. Every event has another meaning and it soon transpired that this was the culmination of an old curse. The elephant was a gandharva who had, in another life, cursed a rishi

A Sem Terra B<u>do</u> Soou Vau Araug Seep.

who had disturbed him. That rishi was reborn as the crocodile, and by another curse that gandharva had become an elephant.

Vishnu says that the elephant of the story represents the human soul of our age, excited by desires, given over to sensual pleasures which are too great to control. There was no salvation for him until he expressed his devotion to Vishnu, who was the only hope for wicked man.

The King, the Pigeon and the Hawk

THERE ONCE WAS A STORY told by Bhishma to Yudhishthira, and it is a story that, once told, will cleanse the teller and the listener of all sin. This is that tale:

There once was a lovely blue pigeon, hotly pursued by a hawk. The pigeon landed, breathless and terrified on the balcony of the home of King Vrishadarbha of Benares.

The gentle king looked with concern at the bird, and taking it into his care, he asked the cause of his distress.

'I am being chased,' said the pigeon, casting down his eyes.

The king spoke quietly and soothed the bird with his kind words. 'Ah, you are a beautiful bird, blue as the sky on a summer's evening, blue as the lotus that has freshly bloomed. Ah, you have eyes like flowers, like the blossoms of an ashoka tree. I will give you protection here. You have come to a place of safety. Rest, dear bird and take comfort.'

Suddenly there was a rush of wings and there, on his balcony, appeared the hawk, irate and breathing as heavily with indignation as the poor pigeon had with fear.

'That,' he said sternly to the king, 'that is my appointed food and you have no right to interfere.'

'Ah,' said the king, 'leave the poor bird. I'll have a boar and some deer dressed for you at once.'

The hawk sniffed. 'Perhaps, my lord,' he said haughtily, 'perhaps you have control over those who call themselves men, but here in the sky you cannot intervene. This is the law of nature. I am hungry. Without the food that this pigeon offers me, I will starve. Boar and deer are the food of men. I want pigeon. Release him at once.'

The king thought for a moment, and then he shook his head. 'I cannot do that,' he said sadly.

Opposite:
The king spoke quietly and soothed the bird with his kind words. 'Ah, you are a beautiful bird,' he said gently.

The hawk sniffed again. 'Well, King Vrishadarbha, if you are so intent on saving the life of this pigeon, perhaps you will exchange some of your own flesh for his. Give me flesh from your body equal to the pigeon's weight and I will allow him to go free.'

Vrishadarbha agreed at once, and taking a blade, he began to cut away at the flesh on his arms and legs, weighing it carefully on a scale against the pigeon. He cut away at his body, and piled the flesh on the scales but they refused to budge. All across the kingdom there rose a great wail as Vrishadarbha cut his way to certain death. At last he was no more than a skeleton, and he threw his whole body on the scale against the pigeon.

There was at once a flash of light, and from the sky appeared a convoy of gods, headed by Indra. The sound of celestial music filled the air and lotus blossoms tumbled down from the heavens. King Vrishadarbha was borne away in a magnificent chariot to take his place in heaven.

It can only be true that whosoever protects another shall receive a good end.

The Ashvin Twins

THERE ONCE WERE TWO BROTHERS, divine twins who were the sons of the sky-god Surya. Their names were Dasra and Nasatya and they were the most exquisitely beautiful boys, looks with which they were blessed into adulthood. The Ashvins were bright and friendly, and they attracted only the best attention wherever they flew. They rode in a gilded carriage – gold which appeared tarnished next to the burnished good looks of the Ashvin twins. They flew quickly and travelled widely, for they sought a place among the pantheon of Hindu gods, an honour which had not yet been accorded.

One day, Dasra and Nasatya were stopped in their travels by the sight of the most delicate and elegant woman, who was taking her bath in a stream near her home. This was Sukanya, or 'Fair-Maid', and she was the wife of the aged rishi Chyavana, who had held her hand in marriage for many years and to whom she had pledged her heart and eternal devotion.

The twins were stunned by the sight of her beauty, and they flew to her side, their pearly smiles flashing as they moved forward to greet her.

Opposite:
The Ashvin twins were handsome boys, and they travelled together, mock fighting and drawing attention to themselves wherever they went.

'You are the most beauteous of all creatures, fair-limbed girl. Who is your father? And how is it that you have been allowed to bathe alone here in these woods?' asked the twins.

'Why I am the wife of Chyavana,' said Sukanya, 'and I bathe here each day.'

The twins shook with laughter. 'How could your father bear for you to give your hand to someone so old and near death. You are the very essence of beauty, fair maiden, and yours should have been the choice of every man.'

'I love Chyavana,' said Sukanya with dignity, preparing to dress.

'Leave your husband,' suggested the Ashvins. 'Come away with us and have a taste of youth. You'll have a life with us and our beauty will be the perfect complement to one another.'

But Sukanya refused their offer and turned to leave her toilet.

But the Ashvins stopped her once again, praying that she should listen to their new request. 'We are medicine men,' they announced, 'and we will make your husband young again, and fair of face. If we do so, fair maiden, will you agree to choose between us a husband for life?'

Sukanya consulted with her husband, who agreed to the plan, and the Ashvins did as they had promised. Within a few moments, Chyavana was at their sides and all three men entered the pool and sank into its depths. There was a pause and then they emerged, all three equal. All three identical.

The three men said in unison, 'Choose among us Sukanya.'

The fair maiden searched carefully for traces of her husband, and when she found them she chose him to be her lord and husband for the remainder of her life.

Chyavana had suffered no indignities, and from this fateful interlude he had had his youth returned to him. He smiled widely, and in gratitude to the Ashvin twins, he promised to win for them the right to sit with the gods, and share in their offerings.

The twins went on their way again, fleet of foot and then high in their gilded chariot. The happy couple lived together in great joy, gods in their own home.

Opposite: 'You are the most beauteous of all creatures, fair-limbed girl. Who is your father? And how is it that you have been allowed to bathe here alone?'

✳   ✳   ✳

GLOSSARY

Aditi   sky goddess and mother of the gods

Adityas   Vishnu, children of Aditi, including Indra, Mitra, Rudra, Tvashtar, Varuna and Vishnu

Agastya   a rishi (sage), leads hermits to Rama

Aghasur   a dragon sent by Kans to destroy Krishna

Agni   the god of fire

Ambalika   daughter of the king of Benares

Ambika   daughter of the king of Benares

Ananda   disciple of Buddha

Ananta   thousand-headed snake that sprang from Balarama's mouth, Vishnu's attendant, serpent of infinite time

Angada   son of Vali, one of the monkey host

Anger-Chamber   room designated for an angry queen

Aniruddha   son of Pradyumna

Anjana   mother of Hanuman

Anshumat   a mighty chariot fighter

Aquila   the divine eagle

Arjuna   the third of the Pandavas

Arundhati   the Northern Crown

Asamanja   son of Sagara

Ashvatthaman   son of Drona

Ashvins   twin horsemen, sons of the sun, benevolent gods and related to the divine twins of Greek and Roman mythology

Ashwapati   Uncle of Bharata and Satrughna

Asparas   dancing girls of Indra's court and heavenly nymphs

Asuras   titans, demons, and enemies of the gods possessing magical powers

Balarama   brother of Krishna

Bali   brother of Sugriva and one of the five great monkeys in the *Ramayana*

Behula   daughter of Saha

Bhadra   a mighty elephant

Bhagavati   Shiva's wife, also known as Parvati

Bhagiratha   son of Dilipa

Bharadhwaja   father of Drona and a hermit

Bharata   one of Dasharatha's four sons

Bhaumasur   a demon, slain by Krishna

Bhima   the second of the Pandavas

Bhimasha   King of Rajagriha and disciple of Buddha

Big-Belly   one of Ravana's monsters

Brahma   creator of the world, mythical origin of colour (caste)

Brahmadatta   King of Benares

Buddha   founder of buddhism, Gautama, avatar of Vishnu in Hinduism

Channa   Guatama's charioteer

Chitambaram   sacred city of Shiva's dance

Chullasubhadda   wife of Buddha-elect (Sumedha)

Chunda   a good smith who entertains Buddha

Daksha   the chief Prajapati

Dasharatha   a Manu amongst men, King of Koshala, father of Santa

Desire   the god of love

Deva   a god other than the supreme God

Devadatta   Buddha's cousin, plots evil against Buddha

Dhrishtadyumna   twin brother of Draupadi, slays Drona

Dilipa   son of Anshumat, father of Bhagiratha

Draupadi   daughter of Drupada

Drona   a Brahma, son of the great sage Bharadwaja

Drupada   king of the Panchalas

Durga   goddess, wife of Shiva

Duryodhana   one of Drona's pupils

Dwarkanath   the Lord of Dwaraka; Krishna

Dyumatsena   King of the Shalwas and father of Satyavan

Ekalavya   son of the king of the Nishadas

Gandhari   mother of Duryodhana

Gandharvas   demi-gods and musicians

Gandjharva   musical ministrants of the upper air

Ganesha   elephant-headed god of scribes and son of Shiva

Ganges   sacred river personified by the goddess Ganga, wife of Shiva and daughter of the mount Himalaya.

Garuda   king of the birds and mount Vishnu, the divine bird, attendant of Narayana

Gautama   son of Suddhodana, also known as Siddhartha

Gopis   lovers of the young Krishna and milkmaids

Great-Flank   one of Ravana's monsters

Guha   King of Nishadha

Hanuman   general of the monkey people

Hari-Hara   Shiva and Vishnu as one god

Hephaistos   the Smith of Heaven

Himalaya   great mountain and range, father of Parvati

Indra   the King of Heaven

Indrajit   son of Ravana

Indrasen daughter of Nala and Damayanti

Indrasena son of Nala and Damayanti

Jambavan a noble monkey

Jatayu king of all the eagle-tribes

Jurasindhu a rakshasa, father-in-law of Kans

Jyeshtha goddess of bad luck

Kaikeyi mother of Bharata, one of Dasharatha's three wives

Kal-Purush the Time-man, Bengali name for Orion

Kali the Black, wife of Shiva

Kalindi daughter of the sun, wife of Krishna

Kaliya a poisonous hydra that lived in the jamna

Kalki incarnation of Vishnu yet to come

Kalnagini serpent who kills Lakshmindara

Kaluda a disciple of Buddha

Kama god of desire

Kamadeva Desire, the god of love

Kans King of Mathura, son of Ugrasena and Pavandrekha

Kanva father of Shakuntala

Karna pupil of Drona

Kashyapa one of Dasharatha's counsellors

Kauravas or Kurus sons of Dhritarashtra, pupils of Drona

Kaushalya mother of Rama, one of Dasharatha's three wives

Keshini wife of Sagara

Khara younger brother of Ravana

Kinnaras human birds with musical instruments under their wings

Krishna the Dark one, worshipped as an incarnation of Vishnu

Kumara son of Shiva and Paravati, slays demon Taraka

Kumbha-karna Ravana's brother

Kunti mother of the Pandavas

Kusha or Kusi one of Sita's two sons

Lakshmana brother of Rama and his companion in exile

Lakshmi consort of Vishnu and a goddess of beauty and good fortune

Lakshmindara son of Chand resurrected by Manasa Devi

Lava son of Sita

Mahaparshwa one of Ravana's generals

Maharaksha son of Khara, slain at Lanka

Mahasubhadda wife of Buddha-select (Sumedha)

Makaras mythical fish-reptiles of the sea

Man-Devourer one of Ravana's monsters

Man-Slayer one of Ravana's counsellors

Manasa Devi goddess of snakes, daughter of Shiva by a mortal woman

Manasha goddess of snakes

Mandavya daughter of Kushadhwaja

Mandodari wife of Ravana

Manthara Kaikeyi's evil nurse, who plots Rama's ruin

Manu Lawgiver

Mara the evil one, tempts Gautama

Markandeya one of Dasharatha's counsellors

Matali Sakra's charioteer

Menaka one of the most beautiful dancers in Heaven

Mitra god of light, Mithra in Iran, Mithras in the Roman world

Mugalana a disciple of Buddha

Nakula Pandava twin skilled in horsemanship

Nala one of the monkey host, son of Vishvakarma

Nandi Shiva's bull

Nataraja manifestation of Shiva, Lord of the Dance

Neta daughter of Shiva, friend of Manasa

Nikumbha one of Ravana's generals

Nila one of the monkey host, son of Agni

Noisy-Throat one of Ravana's counsellors

Pandavas alternative name for sons of Pandu, pupils of Drona

Paramahamsa the supreme swan

Parashurama human incarnation of Vishnu, Rama with an axe

Parvati consort of Shiva and daughter of Himalaya

Passion wife of desire

Pavanarekha wife of Ugrasena, mother of Kans

Pradyumna son of Krishna and Rukmini

Prahasta (Long-Hand) one of Ravana's generals

Prajapati creator of the universe, father of the gods, demons and all creatures, later known as Brahma

Pritha mother of Karna and of the Pandavas

Prithivi consort of Dyaus and goddess of the earth

Purusha the cosmic man, he was sacrificed and his dismembered body became all the parts of the cosmos, including the four classes of society

Pushkara Nala's brother

Pushpaka Rama's car

Putana a rakshasi

Radha the principal mistress of Krishna

Rahula son of Siddhartha and Yashodhara

Rakshasas demons and devils

Rama or Ramachandra a prince and hero of the *Ramayana*, worshipped as an incarnation of Vishnu

Rewati daughter of Raja, marries Balarama

Rhadha wife of Adiratha, a gopi of Brindaban and lover of Krishna

Rishis   sacrificial priests associated with the devas in Swarga

Rituparna   King of Ayodhya

Rohini   Rudra, a name of Shiva

Rudra   Lord of Beasts and disease, later evolved into Shiva

Rukma   Rukmini's eldest brother

Sagara   King of Ayodhya

Sahadeva   Pandava twin skilled in swordsmanship

Sakuni   cousin of Duryodhana

Sambu   son of Krishna

Sampati   elder brother of Jatayu

Santa   daughter of Dasharatha

Sarasvati   the tongue of Rama

Sati   daughter of Daksha and Prasuti, first wife of Shiva

Satrughna   one of Dasharatha's four sons

Satyavan   truth speaker, husband of Savitri

Satyavati   a fisher-maid, wife of Bhishma's father, Shamtanu

Saumanasa   a mighty elephant

Seriyut   a disciple of Buddha

Shaivas or Shaivites   worshippers of Shiva

Shakti   power or wife of a god and Shiva's consort as his feminine aspect

Shamtanu   father of Bhishma

Shankara   a great magician, friend of Chand Sadagar

Shashti   the Sixth, goddess who protects children and women in childbirth

Shesh   a serpent that takes human birth through Devaki

Shitala   the Cool One and goddess of smallpox

Shiva   one of the two great gods of post-Vedic Hinduism with Vishnu

Shudra   one of the four fundamental colours (caste)

Siddhas   musical ministrants of the upper air

Sita   daughter of the Earth, adopted by Janaka, wife of Rama

Skanda   six-headed son of Shiva and a warrior god

Soma   a god and a drug, the elixir of life

Squint-Eye   one of Ramana's monsters

Srutakirti   daughter of Kushadhwaja

Subrahmanian   son of Shiva, a mountain deity

Sugriva   the chief of the five great monkeys in the *Ramayana*

Sukanya   the wife of Chyavana

Suman   son of Asamanja

Sumantra   a noble Brahman

Sumati   wife of Sagara

Sumedha   a righteous Brahman who dwelt in the city of Amara

Sumitra   one of Dasharatha's three wives, mother of Lakshmana and Satrughna

Suniti   mother of Dhruva

Suparshwa   one of Ravana's counsellors

Supranakha   a rakshasi, sister of Ravana

Surabhi   the wish-bestowing cow

Surya   god of the sun

Sushena   a monkey chief

Swarga   an Olympian paradise, where all wishes and desires are gratified

Tall   one of Ravana's counsellors

Tara   Sugriva's wife

Three-Heads   one of Ravana's monsters

Thunder-Tooth   leader of the rakshasas at the seige of Lanka

Tvashtar   craftsman of the gods

Urmila   second daughter of Janaka

Usha   wife of Aniruddha, daughter of Vanasur

Ushas   goddess of the dawn

Vach   goddess of speech

Vajrahanu   one of Ravana's generals

Vali   the cruel brother of Sugriva, dethroned by Rama

Vamadeva   one of Dasharatha's priests

Varuna   ancient god of the sky and cosmos, later, god of the waters

Vasishtha   one of Dasharatha's priests

Vasudev   descendant of Yadu, husband of Rohini and Devaki, father of Krishna

Vasudeva   a name of Narayana or Vishnu

Vedic   mantras, hymns

Vichitravirya   Bhishma's half-brother

Vidura   friend of the Pandavas

Vijaya   Karna's bow

Vikramaditya   a king identified with Chandragupta II

Virabhadra   a demon that sprang from Shiva's lock of hair

Viradha   a fierce rakshasa, seizes Sita, slain by Rama

Virupaksha   the elephant who bears the whole world

Vishnu   The Preserver, Vedic sun-god and one of the two great gods of post-Vedic Hinduism

Vivasvat   the sun

Vrishadarbha   King of Benares

Vrishasena   son of Karna, slain by Arjuna

Vyasa   chief of the royal chaplains

Yadu   a prince of the Lunar dynasty

Yakshas   same as rakshasas

Yama   god of Death, king of the dead and son of the sun

Yasoda   wife of Nand

Yudhishthira   the eldest of the Pandavas, a great soldier

❧ GLOSSARY ❧

Further Reading

Bancroft, Anne, *The Buddhist World* (London, 1989) • Bhattacarji, S., *The Indian Theology: A Comparative Study of Indian Mythology* (Cambridge, 1970) • Dimmitt, C., and van Buitenen, J.A.B., *Classical Hindu Mythology* (Philadelphia, 1978) • Dowson, J., *A Classical Dictionary of Hindu Mythology and Religion* (London, 1961) • Dutt, Romesh C., *Mahabharata and Ramayana condensed* (London, 1963) • Elwin, Verrier, *Myths of Middle India* (Oxford, 1949) • Ions, Veronica, *Indian Mythology* (London, 1967) • Kosambi, D.D., *Myth and Reality* (Bombay, 1962) • Kosambi, D.D., *The Culture and Civilization of Ancient India* (London, 1965) • Knappert, Jan, *An Encyclopedia of Indian Mythology* (London, 1995) • Ling, T., *Buddhism and the Mythology of Evil* (London, 1962) • Marasinghe, M.M.J., *Gods in Early Buddhism* (London, 1974) • Nivedita, Sister, and Ananda K. Coomaraswamy, *Myths of the Hindus and Buddhists* (Canada, 1967) • O'Flaherty, W., *Hindu Myths* (London, 1975) • Roy, Chaudhuri, P.C., et al., *Folk Tales of India* (Delhi, 1969) • Thomas, P., *Epics, Myths and Legends of India* (Bombay, 1973) • *The Ramayana* (London, 1952)

Notes on Illustrations

Page 3 Detail from *Incarnation of Vishnu as a Fish*, from a Devotional Text (British Library, London). Courtesy of The Bridgeman Art Library. **Page 5** Detail from *A Jasrota Prince, Possibly Balwant Singh, in a Riding Expedition*, by Nainsukh (Victoria & Albert Museum, London). Courtesy of The Bridgeman Art Library. **Page 7** Detail from *Krishna Presenting a Lotus to Radha*, illustration to Bhanudatta's Rasamanjari, Basohli, Punjab Hills (Victoria & Albert Museum, London). Courtesy of The Bridgeman Art Library. **Pages 10-11** *Rama and Lakshamana Attacked with Nagapasa*, from the Sangri *Ramayana* (National Museum of India, New Delhi). Courtesy of The Bridgeman Art Library. **Page 12** *Krishna and the Maidens*, Himachal Pradesh, Pahari School (British Library, London). Courtesy of The Bridgeman Art Library. **Page 15** *Akbar Assisting in the Quarrel of the Ascetics*, by Basawan (Victoria & Albert Museum, London). Courtesy of The Bridgeman Art Library. **Page 17** Detail from *Krishna Presenting a Lotus to Radha*, illustration to Bhanudatta's Rasamanjari, Basohli, Punjab Hills (Victoria & Albert Museum, London). Courtesy of The Bridgeman Art Library. **Page 19** *Brahma and Saraswati*, from the Hindu Epic the *Adhyatma Ramayana*, by a Chapra Artist (British Library, London). Courtesy of the Bridgeman Art Library. **Page 21** *Rustam Killing the White Demon*, from the 'Shanama' (Victoria & Albert Museum, London). Courtesy of The Bridgeman Art Library. **Page 22** Detail from *Marriage of Rama and His Brothers* , from the Sangri *Ramayana*, Kulu Mandi (National Museum of India, New Delhi). Courtesy of The Bridgeman Art Library. **Page 25** Detail from *A Jasrota Prince, Possibly Balwant Singh, in a Riding Expedition*, by Nainsukh (Victoria & Albert Museum, London). Courtesy of The Bridgeman Art Library. **Page 27** Detail from *Ladies Visiting a Yogini*, by Uttar Pradesh (Victoria & Albert Museum, London). Courtesy of The Bridgeman Art Library. **Page 29** *The Building of the Fatehpur Sikri Palace* , from the Akbarnama (Victoria & Albert Museum, London). Courtesy of The Bridgeman Art Library. **Page 33** Detail from *Women by a Stream at Night, Watched by Two Noblemen*, by Uttar Pradesh (Chester Beatty Library and Gallery of Oriental Art, Dublin). Courtesy of The Bridgeman Art Library. **Pages 34-5** *A Neglected Lady*, from the 'Prositapatika Nayika' (Victoria & Albert Museum, London). Courtesy of The Bridgeman Art Library. **Page 39** *Surjam Hada Making Submission to Akbar* (Victoria & Albert Museum, London). Courtesy of The Bridgeman Art Library. **Page 41** *Rama Chasing the Golden Deer* (National Museum of India, New Delhi). Courtesy of The Bridgeman Art Library. **Page 43** *Rama and Sita*, from the *Ramayana* (British Library, London). Courtesy of The Bridgeman Art Library. **Page 44** Detail from *Rama and Lakshmana Wandering in Search of Sita*, from the *Ramayana* (National Museum of India, New Delhi). Courtesy of The Bridgeman Art Library. **Page 47** *Madhavanala with a Vine in the Forest from a Madhavanala Kamakandala Series* (National Museum of India, New Delhi). Courtesy of The Bridgeman Art Library. **Page 49** *The Siege of Lanka*, from the *Ramayana* (National Museum of India, New Delhi). Courtesy of The Bridgeman Art Library. **Page 50** Detail from *Rama, Sita (His Wife), Lkshman and Hanuman Holding Rama's Right Foot* (Victoria & Albert Museum, London). Courtesy of The Bridgeman Art Library. **Page 53** *Hanuyman Worshipping Rama, While Sita and Lakshman Look On* (Victoria & Albert Museum, London). Courtesy of The Bridgeman Art Library. **Page 57** *Rama Asks Lakshman to Abandon Sita in a Forest*, from the *Ramayana* (National Museum of India, New Delhi). Courtesy of The Bridgeman Art Library. **Page 59** *Krishna on the Bird Garuda, Overcomes Indra on His Elephant*, from the *Hariansa* (Victoria & Albert Museum, London). Courtesy of The Bridgeman Art Library. **Page 60** *Incarnation of Vishnu as a Fish*, from a devotional text (British Library, London). Courtesy of The Bridgeman Art Library. **Page 65** Detail from *The Infant is Presented to Humayan at Kabul*, from the *Akbar-nama* (British Museum, London). Courtesy of The Bridgeman Art Library. **Page 66** *The Submission of Kaliya, Basohli* (Victoria & Albert Museum, London). Courtesy of The Bridgeman Art Library. **Page 69** *Krishna Lifting Mount Govardhana*, from the *Bhaguvata Purana* (National Museum of India, New Delhi). Courtesy of The Bridgeman Art Library. **Page 71** *The Cow-Girls Bathe in a Lotus Pond While Krishna Lays Out Their Clothes to Dry*, by Uttar Pradesh (Victoria & Albert Museum, London). Courtesy of The Bridgeman Art Library. **Page 73** *Krishna and Radha Walking by the Jumna in the Moonlight Having Exchanged Clothes*, from the *Bhagavata Purana* (Fitzwilliam Museum, University of Cambridge). Courtesy of The Bridgeman Art Library. **Page 75** *Faith, 1912*, by Galileo Chini (Galleria d'Arte Moderna, Florence). Courtesy of The Bridgeman Art Library. **Page 76** *Hanging Scroll of Prabha: Buddha Inaugurating the Practice of Receiving Alms* (Victoria & Albert Museum, London). Courtesy of The Bridgeman Art Library. **Page 81** Detail from *Radha and Krishna Seated in a Grove* (Victoria & Albert Museum, London). Courtesy of The Bridgeman Art Library. **Page 82** *Lady Waiting for Her Lover*, from the *Vasakasaya Nayika* (Victoria & Albert Museum, London). Courtesy of The Bridgeman Art Library. **Page 87** *Prince Salim Surprised by a Lion While Hunting*, Mughal (Christie's, London). Courtesy of The Bridgeman Art Library. **Page 89** *Aurangzeb at Prayer*, Mughal (Bibliothèque Nationale, Paris). Courtesy of The Bridgeman Art Library. **Page 90** *Rajput Princes Hunting Bears While a Mahout and His Elephant Rescue a Fallen Horseman*, from illustrations to the *Large Clive Album* (Victoria & Albert Museum, London). Courtesy of The Bridgeman Art Library. **Page 95** Detail from *Adham Khan, The Murderer of Atgah Khan, Being Thrown from the Walls at Agra, on Akbar's Orders*, from illustrations to the *Akbar-Nama* (Victoria & Albert Museum, London). Courtesy of The Bridgeman Art Library. **Page 97** Detail from *The Grief Stricken Heroine*, from the *Rasamanjari*, attributed to Golu, son of Devidasa (National Museum of India, New Delhi). Courtesy of The Bridgeman Art Library. **Page 101** *The Holy Family of Shiva and Parvati on Mount Kailas* (Victoria & Albert Museum, London). Courtesy of The Bridgeman Art Library. **Page 102** Detail from *Durga in Combat with Mahishasura*, from the Folio of 'Devi Mahatmya' (National Museum of India, New Delhi). Courtesy of The Bridgeman Art Library. **Page 107** *Radha and Krishna on a Bed*, Punjab Hills (Victoria & Albert Museum, London). Courtesy of The Bridgeman Art Library. **Page 108** *A 'Ragini Asvari'*, from a 'Ragamala' (National Museum of India, New Delhi). Courtesy of The Bridgeman Art Library. **Page 111** *Akbar Crossing the Ganges*, from the *Akbar-Nama* (Victoria & Albert Museum, London). Courtesy of The Bridgeman Art Library. **Page 113** *A Party of Elephant Hunters Travelling Through a Landscape* (Victoria & Albert Museum, London). Courtesy of The Bridgeman Art Library. **Page 116** *A'Zam Shah, 3rd Son of Moghul Emperor Aurangzeb with Falcon* (Victoria & Albert Museum, London). Courtesy of The Bridgeman Art Library. **Page 119** *Parasurama Killing Karttavirya*, Arjuna, Chamba or Bilaspur, Himachal Pradesh, Pahari School (National Museum of India, New Delhi). Courtesy of The Bridgeman Art Library. **Page 121** Detail from *Woman Swimming Across a Stream to Her Lover*, from the *Rajasthan* (Victoria & Albert Museum, London). Courtesy of The Bridgeman Art Library. **Page 123** *Akbar Inspecting the Wild Elephant Captured from a Herd Near Malwa*, from the Illustrations to the *Akbar-Nama* (Victoria & Albert Museum, London). Courtesy of The Bridgeman Art Library. **Page 126** *Woman Swimming Across a Stream to Her Lover*, from the *Rajasthan* (Victoria & Albert Museum, London). Courtesy of The Bridgeman Art Library.

Index